Sue Hackman

Fast Forward

LEVEL 3 to LEVEL 4

Hodder & Stoughton

A MEMBER OF THE HODDER HEADLINE GROUP

Acknowledgements

The author and publisher would like to thank the following contributors:

Darren Phillips	• Word Builder sections
Jonathan Rooke	• Detective Reader sections
John Rowley and Dave Watkinson	• Language Workout sections
Kay Hiatt	• Challenge sections
Darren Phillips	• Sentence Builder sections
Kay Hiatt	• Writing Workshop sections

The author and publisher would like to thank the following for:

Copyright text:

p12 *Ten Things Found in a Shipwrecked Sailor's Pocket* © Ian McMillan; p17 *I am David*, Anne Holm. First published 1963 as *David* by Gyldendal, Copenhagen. English translation © 1965, Egmont Children's Books Limited; pp49 and 118 *Fantastic Mr Fox* © Roald Dahl, 1970, Penguin Books; p51 *Cheers! – A True Story* by Regina Michael and *Like Mother, Like Son* by Pauline Cartledge edited by Brian Aldiss © Telegraph Group Ltd; p56 'A Picture of Home' © Bernard Ashley, 1997, from *Stacks of Stories*, Hodder Children's Books; p68 'Spit Nolan' © Bill Naughton, 1961, from *The Goalkeeper's Revenge*, Heinemann; p70 *The Adventures of Huckleberry Finn* by Mark Twain, 1885; p70 *A Christmas Carol* by Charles Dickens, 1842; p71 *Great Expectations* by Charles Dickens, 1860–61; p78 *The Little Ships* © Louise Borden, 1997, Pavilion Books; p78 *The House of Sixty Fathers* © Meindert DeJong, 1956, Puffin Books; p84 'How to Live Forever' © Mary Hoffman, 1997, from *Stacks of Stories*, Hodder Children's Books; pp93–94 *City of the Roborgs* © David Orme, 1996, Nelson Thornes; pp93–94 *Girl Meets Boy* © Derek Strange, 1995, Penguin; pp93–94 *The House of Eyes* © Thomas Bloor, 2002, Hodder Children's Books; pp93–94 *Ghost Dog* © Brandon Robshaw, 2001, Hodder & Stoughton Educational; p96 'A Career in Witchcraft' © Kaye Umansky, 1997, from *Stacks of Stories*, Hodder Children's Books; p102 *The Story of Tracey Beaker* © Jacqueline Wilson, 1992, Corgi Yearling, used by permission of The Random House Group; p102 *The Wreck of the Zanzibar* © Michael Morpurgo, 1995, Heinemann; p102 *Silverwing* © Kenneth Oppel, 1997, Hodder Children's Books; p103 *George, Don't Do That* © Joyce Grenfell, 1977, Macmillan; p103 'But the One on the Right' © Dorothy Parker, 1929, *The New Yorker*; p104 *Fire, Bed and Bone* © Henrietta Branford, 1997, Walker Books Ltd, London; p105 *I am the Cheese* © Robert Cormier, 1977, Penguin; p106 *The Haunting* © Margaret Mahy, 1982, Orion Children's Books.

Copyright photos and images:

p39 *Red Fox Running* © Tom Brakefield, CORBIS; p93 *City of the Roborgs* cover © Nelson Thornes, 1996; p93 *Girl Meets Boy* cover © Pearson Education,1995; p93 *The House of Eyes* cover © Hodder Children's Books, 2002; p93 *Ghost Dog* cover © Hodder & Stoughton Educational, 2001; p119 *Skateboarding* cover © Hodder & Stoughton Educational, 2003.

Copyright illustrations:

pp20–23 © Geoff Jones, 2004, Beehive Illustration; p63 © Alan Down, 2004, Beehive Illustration; pp80–82 © Colin Brown, 2004, Beehive Illustration; pp104, 113 and 114 © Chris Rothero, 2004, Beehive Illustration. Original artwork from *Fast Forward: Level 3 to Level 4*, published in 1999, coloured up by Richard Duszczak, Cartoon Studio Limited, 2004.

Every effort has been made to trace copyright holders of material reproduced in this book. Any rights not acknowledged here will be acknowledged in subsequent printings if notice is given to the publisher.

Orders: please contact Bookpoint Ltd, 130 Milton Park, Abingdon, Oxon OX14 4SB. Telephone: (44) 01235 827720. Fax: (44) 01235 400454. Lines are open from 9.00am – 6.00pm, Monday to Saturday, with a 24 hour message answering service. Email address: orders@bookpoint.co.uk. You can also order through our website www.hodderheadline.co.uk

British Library Cataloguing in Publication Data
A catalogue record for this title is available from the British Library

ISBN 0 340 81585 X

First Edition Published 1999
Colour Edition Published 2004
Impression number   10 9 8 7 6 5 4 3 2 1
Year   2008 2007 2006 2005 2004

Copyright © 2004 Sue Hackman

Typeset by Endangered Species, Essex.
Printed in Italy for Hodder & Stoughton Educational, a division of Hodder Headline Plc, 338 Euston Road, London NW1 3BH.

Contents

Unit Nine

Unit Ten

Answers

Assessment Packs and other Fast Forward books

Please note that Assessment packs are available providing short 'before and after' tests for pupils aiming to move from one level to the next. These tests provide teachers with useful pupil profiles and provide pupils with clear targets. Assessment tasks are built into each masterclass of the **Fast Forward Writing** series.

Fast Forward Level 3 to Level 4	ISBN 0 340 81585 X
Fast Forward Level 3 to Level 4 Assessment Pack	ISBN 0 340 78025 8
Fast Forward Level 4 to Level 5	ISBN 0 340 81586 8
Fast Forward Level 4 to Level 5 Literacy Assessment Pack	ISBN 0 340 80363 0
Fast Forward Level 5 to Level 6	ISBN 0 340 81587 6
Fast Forward Level 5 to Level 6 Literacy Assessment Pack	ISBN 0 340 78025 8
Fast Forward Writing Level 3 to Level 4	ISBN 0 340 81588 4
Fast Forward Writing Level 4 to Level 5	ISBN 0 340 81192 7

TO THE TEACHER

This book offers an intensive programme for raising pupils from Level 3 to Level 4 in literacy. It is a resource for teachers who have been charged with accelerating pupils' progress over a short period, lifting them beyond literal reading and plain writing into a more sophisticated relationship with language.

The content is broadly applicable to pupils at or beyond the end of Key Stage 2. It is suitable for Summer Literacy Schools, for example, or to literacy classes in the years just before or after this. It takes about 50 hours to deliver, though there are opportunities to build extra work into the units, or to select out particular strands.

Secure standards require consolidation, application in different contexts and a continual process of ratcheting up pupils' skills. What this book provides is a core of basic lessons to launch the skills that move a child at Level 3 to Level 4.

What is involved in getting to Level 4?

The move from Level 3 to Level 4 involves a significant qualitative leap. Practice and consolidation of existing skills will not be enough. To move into Level 4, the pupil must –

In reading:

- move beyond literal comprehension to interpretation and appreciation
- use basic inference and deduction
- justify views by pointing to evidence in the text
- know how to locate information.

In writing:

- write for effect
- build extended sentences
- shape and sustain a longer piece of writing
- use commas and speech marks properly
- know the common spelling rules and patterns, including those used in polysyllabic words.

This list will be no surprise for teachers who have studied the feedback of QCA on pupil performance in SATs.

At Level 3, the pupil is a competent reader, being able to decode and understand the literal meaning of texts, and can write in sound basic sentences which are properly punctuated and competently spelt. But at Level 4, this sound competent pupil becomes an active reader and a manipulative writer, consciously engaged in a quest for meaning.

In reading, he or she can read between the lines, filling out the text with imagination, guesswork and inference, sifting and projecting meanings. At this level, the pupil is aware of language as a medium, and can show how it works, finding evidence and explaining effects. He or she sees how different elements in the language pull together to create meaning. It is the end of the one-word answer, because the pupil has noticed the complexity and potential of language.

In writing, the pupil is trying to take control of language to woo the reader, create effects and test the limits of language. He or she searches for a more sophisticated voice in writing, to carry the growing sense of self within him or her at this age. Sentences elongate, digress and qualify their meanings. Paragraphs and writing assignments are varied and given definite shape. New demands are placed on punctuation as the writer builds more complex sentences, and spelling must develop to contain a growing vocabulary.

In short, the pupil has begun to use language as a plastic medium, bending and shaping it for his or her own ends. The defining feature of both reading and writing is the consciousness of language as a tool, and the beginnings of art. The pupil is taking control, and becoming an independent user. If pupils were flowers, they would bloom overnight.

The task of the teacher is to feed this growing capability with the skills and knowledge it needs to make meaning. Pupils moving into Level 4 are pushing at the limits all the time, grappling with voice, structure and convention. They need advice and support. They need a teacher.

Some fortunate children work out the conventions for themselves: their intellect and experience has helped them to internalise the rules of language. They have the benefit of role models, motivation and a repertoire of useful learning strategies.

But some do not work it out for themselves. They lack reading experience, or they are still relatively new to English, or they have not thought to make the connection. Some of them have come through to us in Key Stage 2 having failed to learn first time round. This book is for them. They have the ability, and they have the right to succeed in literacy. It is not too late for any of them. Only the most acute learning difficulties can excuse us from catching up.

About the structure of this book

This book is divided into ten units which take about 5 hours each to deliver. Each unit is divided into six sections as follows:

1 Word Builder

This section contains three parts –

- Spellings to learn: a list of significant high-frequency words for pupils to learn, and be tested on in the following unit.

- Spelling: the introduction of a high-value spelling rule or convention. Securing these simple conventions will deal with the majority of common errors made by pupils at this level.

- Vocabulary: an activity to widen vocabulary and encourage more adventurous choices even from existing vocabulary.

This section on word level work is placed first because it lends itself to a quick-fire, challenging, high-pressure teaching approach to kick off the unit. It is best taught as a quick-fire whole-class activity. Tempting as it is, don't allow pupils to 'get on alone'. It makes a dull start, and isolates pupils within the limits of their existing knowledge. Make use of the pooled knowledge of the class to derive rules, examples and suggestions. This should be the opposite of the quiet start.

2 Detective Reader

This section models for pupils an important reading strategy in one passage, then asks them to use it independently in another.

This is a critical section because it is showing how to deploy reading strategies in the context of a real passage. As far as possible, pupils are drawn in to take an active part in the modelling. Each pupil will have a copy of each passage, but you need to talk it through and show how it's done, and get pupils to talk about the strategies they use. The page has been laid out so that pupils have an aide-mémoire of the strategy, but don't rely entirely on the written page to teach the skill. You need to point, highlight, talk, tell and be absolutely explicit about how you, a good reader, deploy your skills. If you have the resource of large texts, you can point, highlight and gesture how you sift a text for meaning. This may include details which are obvious to you – for example, how you move your eyes, where you look in the passage, how you know something's important – but they are not obvious to the pupil at Level 3. The next step is to get them to take a hands-on approach to the text, for example by using a photocopy of the extract and underlining, highlighting, scanning and selecting, so that they know how it feels to actively seek meaning.

3 Language Workout

This section provides a substantial self-contained activity to practise the reading and writing skills introduced in each unit. As the book progresses, it also revisits earlier reading skills for consolidation. The general approach is one of enquiry and problem-solving, so that language has to be inspected and exploited for a purpose.

The workout is best conducted in small groups, allowing for talk and mutual support. Additional help can be focused on pupils who need most support. The task is to prompt pupils to use the strategies they have been taught, rather than do the work for them. Most of the activities are staged, so that even unsupervised groups have to make contact with an adult as they complete each stage. The key response for unsupervised groups is: 'Describe to me how you went about this task.' And possibly, 'What would have made it easier/more effective?' If you are working alone, these would be very appropriate as debriefing questions in a final plenary, allocating groups to talk through each stage. The emphasis will be on the reading and writing strategies which led successfully to the right answer.

4 Challenge

This is a round of upbeat and easy-to-share word games. Teachers who are using the units as full days should aim to open the afternoon with Challenge. This is a wake-up activity between the substantial Workout which precedes it and the focus required for the Sentence Builder activity which follows.

Set time limits and organise games as competitions, placing pupils in teams. Move back the desks: some of the activities will work as outdoor court games, and others in quiz-show formats.

5 Sentence Builder

This section teaches pupils how to develop their writing at sentence level. Some units address the basic rules of punctuation, and others point to ways of developing more interesting and complex sentences.

The section should be taught as a whole class activity, particularly if pupils can be grouped around a board, so they can point out where punctuation can be inserted or text amended. An OHT with pens will work if space dictates that pupils stay at their desks. Best of all, the activities can be put onto a computer screen so that everyone can try amending and rearranging text. Pupils will pay more attention if they have hands-on opportunities to mark and change texts.

There is rich potential to construct additional activities on screen to edit, correct, extend or explore texts. Digression at this point is probably a good investment if writing is weaker than reading in your class. Boys in particular respond well to lessons packaged as ICT activities.

The skills introduced in this section should be deployed and consolidated in the Writing Workshop which follows.

 6 Writing Workshop

In the first five units, the writing assignments are one-off focused activities which do not require a lot of writing, but do put language under pressure to be concise, focused and evocative. The writing assignments in Units 6–10 are organised as a scaffolded sequence of prompts to write an extended story.

The assignments should deploy the reading and writing skills learnt in the rest of the unit, and this is what you should focus on when you respond to work. In other words, direct your energies on the key skills for attaining Level 4, and don't be side-tracked down interesting but inessential byways. Pupils will be working individually, but allow them to share ideas and co-operate in drafting with others in their group. There is no reason why the work should not be co-written, but you are advised in that case to limit the writing groups to pairs or threes. Quieter and less able pupils are squeezed out if there are more. Some of them might try to sit it out, letting the abler pupils set the pace. Don't let it happen. Make sure everyone is engaged and warn assistants not to do the work for pupils.

Pupils shun extensive redrafting. Computers can help here. Working at a computer takes away the legwork of redrafting, and allows pupils to concentrate on improvement. For this reason, adults should visit pupils in rotation, not to make brief random checks but to chair a discussion in which pupils reflect on their work so far and improve it. Key prompts might be –

- 'Read it aloud to me – which are the most successful moments and why are some moments less successful?'

- 'How did you go about planning/starting/improving this work?'

- 'What has given you most difficulty? What do you need to do to improve/progress this work?'

- 'What advice do you need from me?'

When you look at pupils' work, you will notice errors in basic spelling and punctuation which you must pick up. Don't do proofreading corrections: it only means they will rely on you for accuracy instead of learning the right way to do it. It's better to pick out two or three significant types of repeated error which they will be able to correct for themselves and use again in other work. So, you are likely to spend time on spelling rules rather than one-off spellings, or the conventions of speech punctuation rather than marking in missed punctuation.

Try tackling this in a group setting, as pupils working in pairs and threes listen in to discussion anyway. Other pupils will learn by listening in, and the kinds of errors which prevail at this level are likely to be commonplace. Make use of other pupils by asking them for examples, or to oil the discussion. To make this work, you need to maintain a role which is managerial rather than punitive, developmental rather than corrective. There are three basic steps:

1 Check first by asking them what they already know about the nature of the error. For example:

'What are the two uses of the apostrophe?'

'What rules do you know about speech punctuation?'

'When should you start a new paragraph?'

2 Next, tell them what they don't know or have forgotten. Ask them to write it down so they have a record.

3 Finally, ask them to apply it to their own work. For example:

'Mark in where the paragraph breaks should be.'

'Rewrite this dialogue on the computer and punctuate it in the right way. Call me over when you think you've got it right.'

One of the benefits of teaching Level 4 at this stage is that pupils have often been taught the conventions in the past, but not then picked up. You are building on some previous knowledge. Simplicity and directness is the key. Nine times out of ten, pupils have failed to pick up basic conventions because they have a confusion, and think it is more complicated than it really is. Keep it simple; be explicit; show them an example and give them an aide-mémoire.

You can provide extra support by suggesting how many corrections they are looking for. For example:

- 'There are five paragraphs. Mark in where each one should start.'
- 'Find the three missing capital letters.'

Using Stacks of Stories

The storybook is provided as a resource for studying language in context. Pupils are directed to particular passages to practise their skills. They are asked on occasion to mark the text. Don't stop them. Every instinct tells us to preserve texts for future pupils, but that is not a consideration here. The book is provided specifically for that purpose. In marking the text, pupils will learn how to manipulate text and move selectively around it.

The book is also a resource for reading beyond the exercises. It is not necessary to have read the stories before undertaking the activities, but equally there is no harm if pupils have pre-read them. They will grasp the gist of passages more quickly.

The stories were commissioned by the Library Association and many of them celebrate the place of libraries in the lives of children. If you are using the book as part of a Summer School, an enterprising school librarian will see opportunities for introducing pupils to the library itself.

What else?

This book is a core resource. The teacher is the one to bring it alive and make it work. Brisk, clear, interactive teaching with plenty of opportunity for pupils to participate and develop will deliver results. It won't work if the book is given to pupils as a workbook. They will soon get bored, and we already know that one can't rely on passive reading as the principal learning tool for pupils at this level.

The National Literacy Strategy and the Key Stage 3 National Strategy have developed imaginative ways of engaging whole classes beyond the question and answer routine. Children hold up individual whiteboards made of laminated card to show their attempts at spellings, for example, or choose from flashcards to show whether a word should be 'there' or 'their'. They post words into sound boxes to show what sound the vowels make. They come up to the board to mark texts and choose words. They fall into paired 'ideas sessions' to feed in to the classwork a moment later. They shuffle cards to find a verb to hold up. It does not always have to be the teacher leading by the nose. Indeed, it is better for the pupils if they are obliged to engage in the activities. It's more fun, and less easy to pass through the net. And the teacher can see at a glance who has grasped the idea and who has not.

There is always more that can be done, of course. Summer Schools will wish to find time for outings, visiting writers, and other focal activities. All of these are motivating, and help the group to gel. They help pupils to warm towards their new school and settle into learning more quickly. Sometimes extra-curricular activities can be harnessed into the main objectives. But they will not teach pupils what they don't know and can't do. You have to teach to get that.

Motivation is also a vital part of learning, but like fun, it's not enough on its own to bring pupils up to Level 4. Sweeteners ('Behave well and we'll finish early') are not the answer; indeed they suggest that learning is dull enough to require bribes. Much better are the kind of instant motivators such as team scores, success badges, targets that lie within reach and instant rewards for work well done and recognition for small steps taken. And even then, none of these rewards is as good as public praise for real learning. Your deserved approval is the best motivator. It will go to their heads and their hearts, and keep them coming back for more. It tells them what they already know – that they have made progress in the things that really matter. Theme parks close at 6pm; literacy stays with you.

Maintaining progress

Why is it that pupils sometimes fail to maintain the progress they make in short intensive courses? The answer may be quite simple: they forget, or the skills go rusty for lack of use. Inevitably, short courses cannot offer many consolidation activities to secure confidence and versatility. We launch skills but cannot be sure that pupils will be capable of deploying them in the full range of other contexts.

You can, at least, do something about this. First, this book acts as a reference or aide-mémoire of key points. Also, teachers can be asked to remind and refresh pupils over the following months in the skills introduced now. For this reason, you might wish to copy the contents page of this book to the receiving teacher(s) as an indication of the ground covered.

But the best we can do for pupils who are coming up from behind is to bare the learning process in every classroom. Literacy is an impressive skill, but it is not hard to teach. Pupils are looking for opportunities to learn, even if they affect disdain. It is never too early or too late to teach them what they want to know.

Word Builder

Spellings to learn

Colour, underline or circle any repeated patterns.

Learn them before turning to Unit Two.

Monday

Tuesday

Wednesday

Thursday

Friday

Saturday

Sunday

birthday

holiday

Plurals

Most words add an S when there is more than one object.
For example:

car → cars

dog → dogs

boot → boots

But some words would look and sound funny if just an S was added.

This is because they already end in a hissing or buzzing sound.

So, add ES to these words. For example:

kiss → kisses

box → boxes

lash → lashes

Look at the word bank below. Say each word aloud and decide if it hisses or buzzes or shushes. If it does, then add ES.

Help

- Some people can hear the extra E in the ES ending.

  For example, 'churches'. Can you hear the E?

- Words ending in s, z, sh, ch, x are often followed by ES.

Word Bank

fox.........	salt.........	catch.........
back.........	lunch.........	atlas.........
bin.........	church.........	box.........
waltz.........	bush.........	guess.........
farm.........	crab.........	address.........
fish.........	pen.........	lash.........

YS or IES?

All the words in this word bank end in Y:

Word Bank

boy	monkey	baby	fly
lily	day	stay	story
party	cry	key	toy

But when you make them into plurals by adding an S, look what happens:

Group A

boy	→	boys
monkey	→	monkeys
day	→	days
stay	→	stays
key	→	keys
toy	→	toys

Group B

lily	→	lilies
party	→	parties
cry	→	cries
baby	→	babies
fly	→	flies
story	→	stories

Activity ▷

- Why do the words in Group A end in YS but the ones in Group B end in IES?
- What is the rule?
- Write the rule in your school book.
  1 Add S if...
  2 Change to IES if...

Hint

Look at the letter before the Y.

Vocabulary: Different words, same idea

Synonyms are different words for the same idea.

For example, 'happy' and 'cheerful' are synonyms – they are different words for the same idea.

Activity ▶▶

Find three different ways of saying this sentence by changing the words **pupil**, **laughed** and **joke** each time.

The pupil laughed at the joke.

Draw the diagrams below in your workbook.

Find synonyms for the following words and write them on the arms.

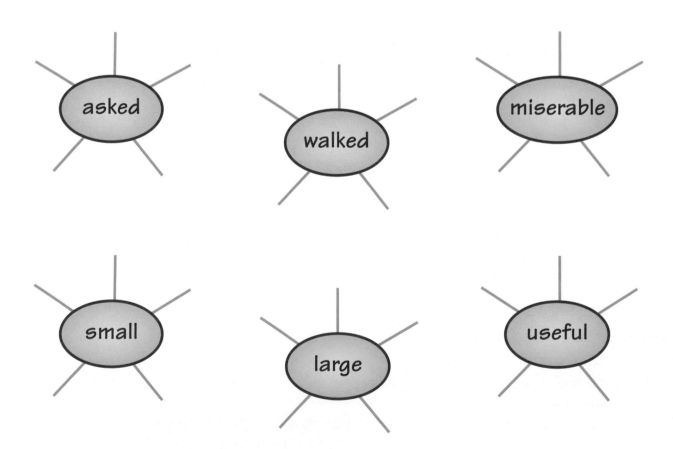

Detective Reader

Finding the bits that really matter

When you are looking for special information:

- some bits tell you what you need to know – these are RELEVANT
- some bits will be about other things – these are IRRELEVANT.

For example: The girl in the passage below has a birthday

1 Suppose you want to find out about the presents she received. Only one sentence is RELEVANT. Which one is it?

2 Suppose you want to find out about her mum's new boyfriend and what she thinks about him. Go through the sentences and decide if they are relevant or irrelevant. Write 'relevant' or 'irrelevant' in each box – there is one box for each sentence. Two have been done for you.

3 Next to the relevant sentences, write down why they are relevant.

IRRELEVANT – nothing about her mum's boyfriend here.

RELEVANT – 'Total Drip' tells us she dislikes him.

I had cards and stuff from The Body Shop and music tokens and chocolates and a game and some felt tips from my friends – nothing at all from my father.

'Don't say he's forgotten again', Mum said wearily, 'I'll phone him up – it's too bad of him.'

'No, it's great, because he'll feel so guilty when you tell him he might send me a great big cheque,' I said.

I can act really cool about my parents splitting up.

Just so long as she doesn't muck things up with a boyfriend.

There's this Total Drip who works at the library and fusses round her.

He was fussing in overdrive when Mum and I arrived at the park where the Fun Day was being held, setting up stalls and dashing around being drippily keen and enthusiastic.

I assumed his nerdy woolly cap was his personal choice of headgear, but Mum told me he was being a wally.

Agent X-Libris

We need to find a new librarian. Your mission is to check out Mr Smike in the story 'A Career in Witchcraft' (in the *Stacks of Stories* book). Would he make a good school librarian?

Activity ▷

1 As you read, watch out for RELEVANT information and highlight it.

2 Choose the six most revealing bits of information and write the exact words in the labels, explaining what they reveal about Mr Smike.

Mr Smike would/would not make a good librarian because...

3 Now complete your report in the box on the right:

Well done, You have completed your first mission!

Language Workout

Catch a thief!

During the summer holidays there is a break-in at the school. All the cups have been stolen from the school's trophy cabinet.

Several people saw the thief. This is what they told the police:

I saw a white Escort van pull up. A man in blue overalls got out. I thought he was going to deliver a package. As he walked up the main steps, I noticed a slight limp. He was about 5 foot 10 inches tall. The other thing I noticed was that he was wearing brand new DMs. When he saw me, he got back in his van and drove off. It looked suspicious. I didn't get his number.

Caretaker, Ian Marten

It was about 10.00am. I was tidying the art room. It overlooks the main block. I heard a noise like muffled glass breaking. I looked out and saw a man, in his mid-30s. He had short hair and he was going bald. Looked a bit like Phil Collins. He was carrying a very big bag. He was wearing a blue fleece top and Nike trainers.

Art teacher, Emma Holland

I saw a white man while I was waiting for Mummy. He had a big bag. He had those trainers that have flashing lights when you walk. He crossed the playground and got into a white car. He had an earring with a skull or something like that. He also had writing on his knuckles, like a tattoo. He was about as tall as my daddy, and he is very tall!

5-year-old Louise Thomas

I saw this bloke. He asked me where he could find the caretaker. He was about 5 feet 9 inches tall. He was well built, solid, like a rugby player. He had bright blue eyes. He had a bunch of keys that had a long wooden key fob, with a name on it – 'Alan', I think it was. He had a big black bag with him.

Window cleaner, Jed Soley

Activity ▷▷

- Compare the descriptions and decide what definite information you have about the thief.
- Make a sketch of the thief and label it.
- Write a paragraph describing the man you are looking for.

Suspects

The police come up with four suspects who fit the description.
You bring them in for questioning at the police station:

Suspect 1 – Jake Murphy

Height: 5 foot 10 inches
Age: 36
Hair: Black
Eyes: Blue
Job: Club owner
Home: Opposite school

On his person:

Police Record:
• Shoplifting 1995
• Theft 1997, 2002
Car(s):
• Grey Mercedes
• White Escort found in garage opposite school.
Alibi: Driving to a meeting in North London.
Other evidence:
• Made 2 long phone calls on his mobile around 10.00am (checked and confirmed).

Suspect 2 – Donald 'Deadleg' Malone

Height: 5 foot 11 inches
Age: 32
Hair: Dark
Eyes: Blue
Job: Handyman
Home: 15 minutes from school

On his person:

Police Record:
• Shoplifting 1986 & 2002
• Theft 1987, 91, 92, 93, 96, 02
Car(s):
• A red Escort estate
• Uses a white Escort Van for work.
Alibi: In bed at home, sleeping off a hangover, met a friend in Red Lion Pub at 12.00pm.
Other evidence:
• A bag with a jemmy and other tools found in garage at his home.

Suspect 3 – 'Maggie' Pearson

Real name: Ulrike Amanda Pearson
Height: 5 foot 9 inches
Age: 34
Hair: Blonde (but record of using disguises)
Eyes: Blue
Job: Evening job at supermarket
Home: Opposite school
Police Record:
• Been questioned by police – never charged.
Alibi: Took son to school at 8.45am. No alibi for 10.00am. Ate lunch at the 'Rumbling Tum' cafe at midday, just around the corner from school.
Other evidence:
• Doesn't drive.

On her person:

Suspect 4 – BB West

Height: 6 foot
Age: 34
Hair: Dark usually worn long.
Eyes: Hazel
Job: Local DJ
Police Record:
• Theft 1982, 91, 97, 98, 03
Alibi: Visited his Gran's grave at 11.00am. Could have made journey from school to cemetery in 1 hour.
Car(s):
• White Vauxhall Astra Van.
Other evidence:
• Known to have serious gambling problem.

On his person:

You need to charge ONE of your suspects in the next half-hour, or you have to let them all go.

In your group discuss each suspect in turn. Put your information in a grid similar to the one below.

Name of suspect	Evidence of guilt	Evidence of innocence
Jake		
Deadleg		
Maggie		
BB West		

Who do you think did it?

Role Play

- Choose someone to be the suspect.
- Choose two people to be the prosecuting team.
  (Your job is to persuade the jury that he's guilty.)
- Choose two people to be the defending team.
  (Your job is to persuade the jury that he's innocent.)
- Four people act as the witnesses from page 7.
- The rest be the jury.
- The teacher is the judge.

This is the order:

1 The judge explains the crime to the jury.

2 The witnesses are questioned in turn by the prosecution and the defence.

3 The suspect is questioned by the prosecution and by the defence.

4 The jury can ask any extra questions.

5 The prosecution and defence take turns to sum up the case for and against the suspect.

6 The jury vote.

See the answers section on page 120.

Challenge

Word strings

Can you name all five vowels?

Some words have two vowels next to each other. For example:

- b**ee**
- r**ai**n

The game

String together letters in the grid to make as many words as you can containing **two vowels next to each other**.

Rules

- The letters must touch.
- Use letters once only in a word.
- You have ten minutes.
- The group to get most is the winner.

S	T	B	R	P
U	A	E	E	S
T	I	V	O	P
N	R	U	I	L
I	A	T	O	O

These are the possible vowel combinations:

aa	ea	ia	oa	ua
ae	ee	ie	oe	ue
ai	ei	ii	oi	ui
ao	eo	io	oo	uo
au	eu	iu	ou	uu

Activity ▷▷

- Can you think of an example for each vowel combination?
- Which ones are never used in English?

Sentence Builder

Sound effects in language

Have you heard of the film *Chitty Chitty Bang Bang?* In what way does the title sound like the vintage car in the film?

Here are some more words that sound interesting. What noises do they describe?

vroom   **chortle**   **clatter**   **boom**   **tinkle**

Onomatopoeia is when a word sounds like the thing it describes.

- Can you think of five more examples?

Activity ▷▷

In your workbook finish this poem using onomatopoeic words:

Sounds in the classroom

The _____ of the chairs,

The boom of the _____,

_____,

_____

And then the silence_____.

Alliteration is when a string of words starts with the same sound. For example:

- The **w**ind is **w**hispering in the **w**illows.

Why was W a good sound to repeat?

Activity ▷▷

In class, think of a describing word which alliterates with your name. For example:
- Silly Sally
- Perfect Peter

Writing Workshop

Read this poem:

Ten Things Found in a Shipwrecked Sailor's Pocket

1 A litre of sea.

2 An unhappy jellyfish.

3 A small piece of a lifeboat.

4 A pencil wrapped around with seaweed.

5 A soaking feather.

6 The fifth page of a book called swimming is easy.

7 A folded chart showing dangerous rocks.

8 A photograph of a little girl in a red dress.

9 A gold coin.

10 A letter from a mermaid.

by Ian McMillan

Activity ▶

- Read and discuss this poem with a partner. Think about your reaction to each item in turn.
- Why is each item in his pocket?
- What do the items tell us about the sailor?
- Plan a poem of your own. Work in groups using one of these titles, or one of your own:

  Ten Things Found in a Lost Astronaut's Pocket
  Ten Things Found in a Happy Princess's Pocket
  Ten Things Found in a Sad Clown's Pocket
  Ten Things Found in a First Division Footballer's Pocket
  Ten Things Found in a Magician's Pocket
  Ten Things Found in a Busy Mum's Pocket

- Produce a list of items on a spare piece of paper.
- Select the best ten and write them onto a planner like the one below.

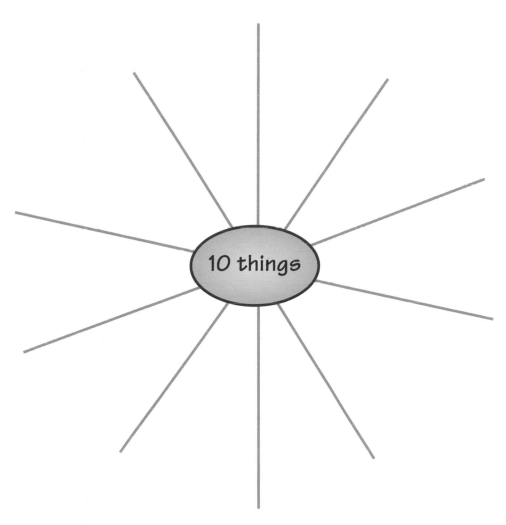

- Add more information about each item.
- Try to make the person reading your poem smile, laugh, or feel sad.
- Spell check now!
- Write it out, or type it, then print it. Illustrate if you have time.

Good Luck!

Word Builder

Spelling check

Test yourself on the spellings from Unit One.

1 _____   6 _____

2 _____   7 _____

3 _____   8 _____

4 _____   9 _____

5 _____

Unit Two spellings

Colour, underline or circle any repeated patterns.

Learn them before starting Unit Three.

January

February

March

April

May

June

July

August

September

October

November

December

Doubling consonants – the long and the short of it

Vowels can say their own names, for example, the A in DAY.

Vowels can say a short sound, for example, the A in CAT.

The way to mark a sound is to put a line over it if it says its own name (a long sound) and bendy line if it is short. For example:

- plāte (says its own name)
- dăd (short sound).

Activity ▶▶

Write out these words and put the right kind of lines on vowels.

cat   cave   flavour   late

Try it with the letter O.
For example:
- **hōle** (says its own name)
- **cŏt** (short sound).

more   phone   doll   top

Can you think of 2 more words with a long E? See the example below:
e.g. **peel**

2 more words with a short E:
e.g. **pet**

2 more words with a long I:
e.g. **write**

2 more words with a short I:
e.g. **pin**

2 more words with a long U:
e.g. **cute**

2 more words with a short U:
e.g. **cut**

- Why does WRITING have one T, but WRITTEN has two?
- Why does DINING have one N, but DINNER has two?
  The answer lies in the vowel sound. Can you work out the rule?

Double the letter if...

Vocabulary: Shades of meaning

Each word in the square links to three words outside the square.

Can you work out which?

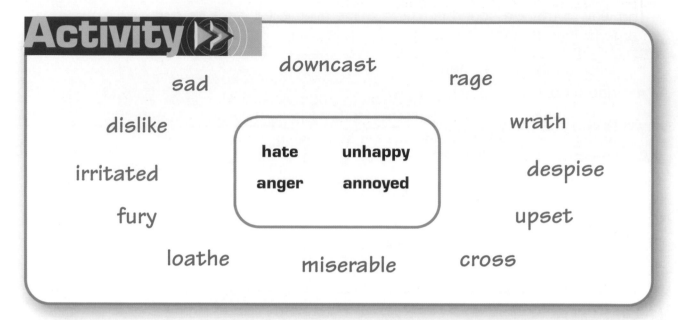

There are slight differences in meaning even between similar words.

Some words are stronger than others. Write out the words below in order of strength, putting 1 next to the strongest, 4 next to the weakest, etc.

A	irritated	furious	cross	angry
B	cold	cool	lukewarm	freezing
C	sad	low	miserable	unhappy

Now find five examples of words with three shades of meaning:
mild, **medium**, **strong**.

Detective Reader

Building up a picture

This passage is about a boy called David.

David pressed himself even more closely against the wall. It was the man; the faint sleepy yellow light from the guard-room shone for a moment on his face as he passed the window. He went up to the guard, and David suddenly felt quite empty inside and was sure he would be unable to move when the time came. Then he saw before him the endless succession of days, months and years that would pass if he did not. The waiting would kill him in the end, but it might take years. And it would grow worse and worse, all the time. David clenched his teeth so hard that he felt the muscles of his throat grow taut. Then the man struck a match.

Nineteen, twenty – the half minute would be up when he had counted slowly to thirty. David set his foot in a gap higher up the barbed wire. When would the searchlight come? They could not be certain of hitting him in the dark … and if they did not hurry he would be over.

A moment later he had touched the ground on the other side, and as he ran he said angrily to himself, 'What a fool you are! There's plenty of ground to cover yet – all this great flat stretch without so much as the stump of a tree for shelter. They'll wait till you've nearly touched the thicket … they'll think it more amusing if you believe you've almost got to safety.'

From *I Am David* by Anne Holm

Activity

- Make a list of all the things that hint to you what time of day it is.
- Make a list of all the things that tell you how David is feeling.
- Sum up his feelings.

Activity ▶

Make a list of all the things you are told about the place David is in and where things are. Complete the sketch of the scene that has been started here.

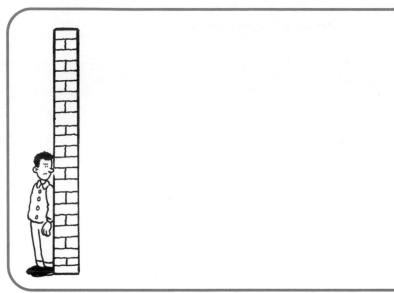

- Work out what David is up to. When you think you know write it here.

    David is trying to:

    _____

    _____

    _____

- Now justify or prove your answer by finding five words or phrases to support it. An example is done for you.

Word or phrase	How it justifies my answer
Guard-room	suggests he is under guard

Agent X-Libris

Reports are coming in about a girl in Cleator Moor who has travelled back in time. Your mission is to bring back a detailed account of the town library in 1911 so that future generations will know its history. Go to 'Time Slide' by Julia Jarman in the *Stacks of Stories* book. Highlight all the relevant information. Please present your report in a form similar to the one below. Good luck!

TOP SECRET

1. Staff responsibilities and attitudes

_____

2. Main similarities to a library today

_____

3. Main differences from a library today

Activity ▶▶

From what you have read, draw a layout of the library as it would have appeared in 1911.

Language Workout

Lost

On Sunday, Bharat Patel aged 16, and his sister Suraj, 10, were taken to the circus by their parents. It was a birthday treat for Suraj.

On Monday, Bharat was supposed to be going camping with his youth club. 9.10am – Mrs Thornton, the youth club leader, called Mrs Patel – Bharat had not turned up!

Mrs Patel called the police to let them know that Bharat was missing.

The police said that they would keep an eye out for Bharat. Information started to pour in…

8.00am   9.00am   10.00am

The Plot thickens

Michael and Suzy Napper saw Bharat on the bus, heading up the High Street towards Park Road. This was at 9.35am.

10.10am – a report came in from a police car at the junction of High St and Park Road. Bharat had been seen getting into a taxi, headed up Park Road.

At 10.40am, the police and Mrs Patel returned home. On the kitchen table was a book about animals. Some half-eaten carrots and mud were on the floor...

10.43am a couple driving on Ash Road phoned in – they had seen a zebra on the zebra crossing!

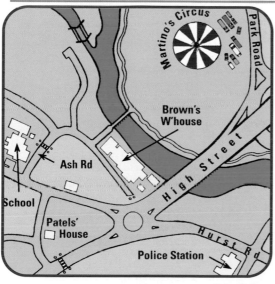

Activity ▶

1 Use the map to follow the route taken by Bharat as reports come in.

2 Copy this timeline on to a sheet of paper to record where you think Bharat was, and when.

11.00am   **12.00pm**

10.44am – Martino's Circus reported that a zebra had gone missing.

11.00am – Mrs Patel told the police that Bharat and Suraj went to the circus last night, and loved the zebras.

Police Inspector McAteer is now quite sure why Bharat did not turn up for the camping trip.

What has Police Inspector McAteer worked out?

He decides to put a bulletin on the local radio, asking for the help of the public.

• You must write and then tape this bulletin, which must be no more than one minute long.

Help ▶▶

Use these starters to help you:

• Here is an important police message…
• Bharat Patel has gone missing in…
• Bharat is…
• We believe that…
• He was last seen at…
• Anyone with information should…

Closing in...

11.35am – A cyclist reported banging noises coming from Brown's Warehouse near the river.

11.40am – A fight was reported in the Post Office in the High Street.

12.00pm – Some carrots were found on the towpath near Brown's Warehouse.

Help >>

Use these starters to help you:
* Make your way to...
* Take the following route:
* First, turn...

Activity >>

* Work out where Bharat is. Look at all the information, and work out what is RELEVANT and what is IRRELEVANT.
* Use the map to give clear directions to the police cars to get from the police station to where you think he is.
* Try out your directions by reading them to another group to see if they find the right spot.

Challenge

Ball game

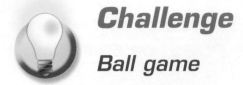

This is an outdoor game. Draw a chalk grid on the floor like the one below. Each square is about 1/2 metre square.

1 Get into fours. Two stand at the top of the grid. Two stand at the bottom.

2 Build words letter by letter by bouncing a ball on the right letters. You only get the letter it lands on. Each letter is worth 1 point. Your turn ends when you have made a word or you can't go.

3 You score points for each letter in the word. For example, 'it' = 2 points; 'party' = 5 points.

4 The first group to get 15 points is the winner.

- Did you notice which were the most used letters?
- Why do you think they were popular?

T	A	C
L	R	E
M	I	T
K	H	O
C	U	Y
O	P	A
N	E	S

Sentence Builder

Building tension

- Read pages 129–132 of 'Mozart's Banana' in the *Stacks of Stories* book. In this passage there is an exciting chase between a horse and a library van.

  To keep up the excitement, the writer has used these methods:

A Short sentences to make it sound breathless.

B Lists of things happening one after another to make it feel action-packed.

C A single phrase in a paragraph on its own, to give it shock value.

D Using dramatic words and comparisons to make it sound exciting.

E Description of other events to relieve the excitement.

Activity ▷▷

- Which methods are used in each of these sentences?
  Mark them A, B, C, D or E. Some use more than one method.

  The horse went past like a thunderbolt.

  A crazy horse charging under the railway, across the slip road and straight out into six lanes of traffic.

  THE MOTORWAY!

  All the other children were running out to see what was going on. Teachers were shouting and parents were waving their arms about.

- Now look through pages 129–132 in *Stacks of Stories* and label other examples.

- In groups, write a description of a short car chase, using the methods shown above.

Writing Workshop

This recipe is written the same way as most recipes.

Baked Beans on Toast

Ingredients

Small tin of baked beans
Two slices of bread
Butter

Method

1 Open tin of beans and pour them into a small saucepan.
2 Place the bread in a toaster and cook until golden brown.
3 Heat the beans for 5 minutes.
4 Butter both slices of toast.
5 Pour the hot beans on top of the toast.

Fill in the rules:

Recipes are written in this order:

1 _____

2 _____

3 _____

The ingredients are always written in this way:

1 _____

2 _____

3 _____

The instructions are always written in this way:

1 _____

2 _____

3 _____

We can write more interesting recipes than this one!

How about:

- A Recipe for a Great Party
- A Recipe for a Great Football Match
- A Recipe for a Fantastic Disco
- A Recipe for a Ghost Story
- A Recipe for My First Day at My New School

Plan your recipe, and write it in the blank recipe box.

Title

Ingredients

Method

Useful words:

Mix   Find   Beat   Heat   Cool   Roast   Stir

Bake   Whisk   Leave   Remove   Slice   Add

Word Builder

Spelling check

Test yourself on the spellings from Unit Two. Write down the months of the year below:

1 _____   7 _____

2 _____   8 _____

3 _____   9 _____

4 _____   10 _____

5 _____   11 _____

6 _____   12 _____

Colour, underline or circle repeated patterns in the words on the page opposite.

Learn the spellings before starting Unit Four.

To make life easier:

Cross off the ones you are sure you know.

Keep testing the ones you get wrong, and take them home to learn.

Unit Three spellings

one	sixteen
two	seventeen
three	eighteen
four	nineteen
five	twenty
six	thirty
seven	forty
eight	fifty
nine	sixty
ten	seventy
eleven	eighty
twelve	ninety
thirteen	hundred
fourteen	thousand
fifteen	million

Prefixes

Prefixes go **in front of** a word.

Prefixes don't change the spellings of words, but they do add new meanings.

'Pre' is a prefix! It means 'before'.

Activity ▷

- What do you think **prehistoric** means?
- Can you think of other words starting with 'pre' and mean before?
- Look in the dictionary to find words with the following prefixes. See if you can work out what each prefix means:

Re   Octo   Port   Anti   Cent   Trans   Uni   Circ   Scrip

Suffixes

A suffix is added **at the end of** a word. Like the prefix, it adds new meaning, but it can also change the spelling.

Activity ▷

Below are some suffixes.
- List three words which end in each suffix.

hood   ing   ed   ly   ful
est   able   less   ness
ship

Activity ▷

- Which suffix means:
- happened in the past?
- without?   – the most?
- full of?
- Can you work out what the others mean?

Suffixes may affect spellings if the original word ends in an E.

Lose the E if...

- the suffix begins with a vowel
- the suffix is a Y.

Add 3 different suffixes to each of the words below:

like   arrive   excite   love   use
care

Vocabulary

The words we choose show our opinions and attitudes.

If I like him

He's a cheeky lad.

If I loathe him

He's a rude boy.

Almost 100 people turned out to greet him.

Less than 100 people turned up.

He's clever and well-behaved.

_____
_____

He's late. He must have been held up.

_____
_____

- Think of a 'loathe' saying for the last two pictures and write them in your workbook.
- Can you make up some 'like + loathe' sayings?

Detective Reader

Fact finding

You don't have to read every word to find the information you need.

To find facts quickly, you can:

- Look for headings that tell you what is there.
- Look at the opening sentence of each paragraph. This key sentence often tells you what is in the rest of it.
- Look for words you expect to find in it.
- Look for big ideas without reading every word.

Activity ▷

You want to find out about AUSTRALIA, without reading every word.

1 The title is 'The Seven Continents'.
Is Australia likely to be mentioned? How do you know?

2 Scan the opening sentence of each paragraph.
Only one paragraph does **not** mention Australia. Can you tell which one it is just by scanning the extract?

3 Think of three words that are very likely to be used in information about Australia. Write them down.

4 Skim through without reading every word, and look for the three key words.

5 Underline all the sentences that tell you something about Australia.

Help ▷▷

Skimming is like fast reading. Run your eyes along the lines quickly in the usual way.

Scanning is like ice skating. Throw your eyes around the page like a skater around a rink. Watch for special words or features.

The Seven Continents

There are seven continents in the world: North America, South America, Europe, Asia, Australia, Antarctica and Africa. Europe and Africa each have more than 40 countries in them. Australia is such a large country that it is called a continent.

Continents have different climates. Antarctica is a frozen region and only scientists live there for long periods of time. In the middle of Australia there is a hot desert and people like to live on the coast where there is water and cool breezes. Even though it is cooler there, the sun is so strong that people must wear hats and cream to protect themselves from the rays.

Different continents have different wildlife. Africa and Asia have a wide variety of animals such as tigers and elephants. South America is the home of the condor and the jaguar. Australia has kangaroos, while Antarctica has penguins.

Continents are famous for their foods. North America is the home of the hamburger and South America grows cocoa beans from which chocolate is made. Spices such as cinnamon and ginger come from Asia and kiwi-fruit is grown in Australia.

Antarctica is a continent, but the Arctic is not. This is because there is no land under the Arctic ice. Beneath the Antarctic are mountains buried in snow.

Agent X-Libris

URGENT! HQ needs information about Somalia from 'A Picture of Home' by Bernard Ashley in *Stacks of Stories*. Gather information about Somalia in peacetime and in war. There's no time to read every word. Look for key sentences and key words such as **Somalia** and **home** and **peace** and **war**. Stop only if the information looks relevant.

- Build up two lists, one for Somalia at peace and one for Somalia at war. Useful pages are **41**, **42**, **45**, **47**, **48**, **51** and **54** but there are lots of other clues.
- Use your list to write a short passage about Somalia in the style of 'The Seven Continents' passage above.

Language Workout

So you think you can read the news?

- You are a TV news reporter on the spot with a TV camera crew.
- You are going to make a live 90 second bulletin for the midday news.
- Read what happens below.
- You have 15 minutes to prepare your report. Use a video if you have one.
- Your teacher will count down to transmission time. Follow the advice in the Help box.

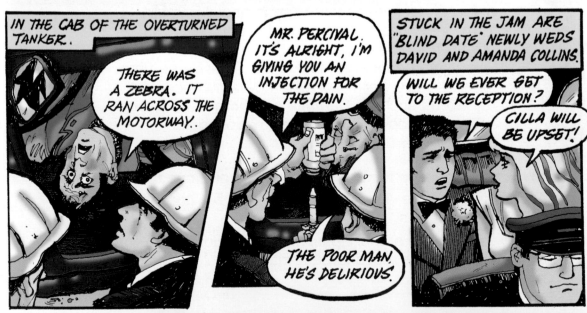

Help ▶▶

Organising a live news report

1 Grab the viewers' attention right away:

A major motorway was blocked this lunchtime...

2 Explain what happened:

The accident happened at 9.30 when a tanker...

3 Tell what the immediate consequences were:

Within minutes,...

4 Tell some interesting aspects of the story:

Among those trapped in the jam were...

5 Summarise what will happen next:

Police say they will...

6 Sign off:

This is . . . . . . for . . . . . . at Junction 3 on the . . . . . .

The afternoon bulletin

It is now afternoon and events continue to unfold in the motorway story.

- You have travelled from the motorway to the hospital. The power cut means the hospital is under pressure.
- You have just 10 minutes to prepare your next bulletin. This time the bulletin is just 30 seconds long.

The early evening news

It is now early evening and things are getting back to normal.

People are coming home from work and haven't heard about the story yet.

There are some new things to tell them about, too.

- You have 10 minutes to prepare your last bulletin of 60 seconds.

Challenge

Quick-fire quiz

You will need a dictionary to help you.

Which **a** works in mid-air?

Which **b** can you dip into a cup of tea?

Which **c** is a hot, spicy meal?

Which **d** works underwater?

Which **e** knows a lot about something?

Which **f** keeps you warm?

Which **g** is absolutely brilliant!

Which **h** can be dark, light, straight or curly?

Which **i** can fly, crawl and might even hop?

Which **j** is really sweet and made from fruit?

Which **k** is used to slice, cut, chop and dice?

Which **l** can carry people up and down?

Which **m** can come from goats, cows and even sheep?

Which **n** can be found on rulers?

Which **o** propels a boat forward?

Which **p** is found attached to a flower?

Which **q** can be found at a bus stop?

Which **r** might you receive if you return a lost item?

Which **s** keeps your hair clean?

A _ _ _ _ _ _ _ _ _ _ _

B _ _ _ _ _ _ _

C _ _ _ _ _

D _ _ _ _ _

E _ _ _ _ _ _

F _ _ _ _

G _ _ _ _ _ _

H _ _ _ _

I _ _ _ _ _ _

J _ _

K _ _ _ _ _

L _ _ _

M _ _ _ _

N _ _ _ _ _

O _ _

P _ _ _ _ _

Q _ _ _ _ _

R _ _ _ _ _ _

S _ _ _ _ _ _ _

The answers are on page 120. **Well done!**

Now make up your own clues for the last seven letters:
Swap worksheets with another group and guess each other's answers.

Which **t**	?	T	
Which **u**	?	U	
Which **v**	?	V	
Which **w**	?	W	
Which **x**	?	X	
Which **y**	?	Y	
Which **z**	?	Z	

Sentence Builder
Expanding sentences

Activity ▷

- How could you expand the sentence below?

Add an **adverb** that says how he ran.

Add an **adjective**.

Add a **description** of the path he took.

The fox ran for cover.

Add a **phrase** to tell us how the fox was feeling, or what he was up to.

Add in where he took cover and what he did next.

Activity ▷

Expand these sentences to write a powerful paragraph:

HUNTED!
The fox stopped.
He heard the bark of dogs.
The hunters appeared.
They set the dogs on the fox.
The fox ran for cover.

(Finish this with a sentence of your own.)

- You could expand the sentence, too, by using 'but', 'because', or 'and' at the end, and then adding a new phrase.

Writing Workshop

Daft diaries

Activity ▶▶

Read this daft diary

- What makes this diary unusual?
- What makes it funny?
- What time does the diary begin and what time does it end? Why did it start and end at these times?

Now choose a different animal such as a bored budgie, a snooty cat, a dim dog, a pet mouse or even a brand-new baby!

1 Think of things it would do in the course of a day and a night. Write the name of the animal in a circle and list the activities around it.

2 Think of the times when your creature would meet up with a human. Is there anything the creature would do to annoy the human? Add ideas to your plan.

3 Now add some extra details to make your reader laugh.

4 If your creature could write, how might it sound? For example: snarling? cheerful? grumpy? bossy?

5 Now write your own daft diary entry.

The Hamster's Diary

by Martin Wiley

11 pm Wake up.

11.30 pm Get out of bed.

Midnight Walk around cage.

1 am Eat breakfast (nuts again)

2 am Re-arrange sawdust.

3 am Start jogging on wheel.

4 am Still jogging on wheel (needs oiling)

4.30 am Soon be fit enough for London Marathon (hamster section)

5 am Large human crashes downstairs, switches on bright lights. Human RATTLES CAGE and SHOUTS. He is wearing striped suit tied with string.

7 am Feeling tired, get into bed.

7.30 am Large and small humans come downstairs. They shout, play music, punish eggs in boiling water and cut up bread with a knife.

9 am Humans disappear.

Peace. Sleep.

Word Builder

Spelling check

Test yourself on the spellings from Unit Three. Write them next to each number:

1 _____	11 _____	30 _____
2 _____	12 _____	40 _____
3 _____	13 _____	50 _____
4 _____	14 _____	60 _____
5 _____	15 _____	70 _____
6 _____	16 _____	80 _____
7 _____	17 _____	90 _____
8 _____	18 _____	100 _____
9 _____	19 _____	1000 _____
10 _____	20 _____	1,000,000 _____

Unit Four spellings

Some of the trickiest words are easy to learn if you think about their 'family' words. What is it besides the spellings that makes each group a family?

A   which   why   where

B   where   there   here

C   they   them   their

D   ear   hear   heard

- Can you think of other family groups of words?

The long A

There are three main ways to spell the long A sound:

AI as in R**AI**N • AY as in P**AY** • A_E as in T**A**P**E**

1   Which two usually come at the end of words?

2   Which usually comes in the middle of words?

List four words using each spelling: AI, AY, A_E.

Help ▶▶

Listen closely to compare the sounds of the AY words (in the left column) with the others (on the right).

• Can you hear the very small extra sound of the Y? If you can hear it, it will help you to make the right choice of spelling.

play	plain	say	same
layer	lane	daylight	date

Vocabulary: Refining words

Some words are more general than others and have groups within them. Here is a word pyramid for ANIMALS:

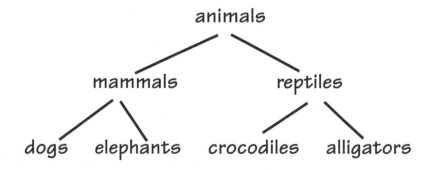

Activity ▶▶

• Make word pyramids for:
  VEHICLES   FOOD
  WEAPONS   SPORTS
  Put in as many layers as you can.

Detective Reader

A telling choice of words

Strong feelings in the writer can sometimes be seen in his or her choice of words.

In fact, writers choose words in order to influence or **bias** the reader.

Read this point of view and then complete the activity:

Activity ▷

The idea of building a new road to bypass the town is absolutely brilliant. It will certainly make it easier to drive around the town centre. The scruffy woodland that will need to be removed to make way for the road is a small price to pay.

- Find a word which says directly that the bypass is a good idea.
- Find a word that suggests there can be no question about the value of the bypass.
- Find a word that paints an unpleasant picture of life without the bypass.
- Find two ways the writer suggests that the destruction of the woodland hardly matters.

The writer of the next article wants to make people angry about the sale of unhealthy food:

The death of two more children from mad cow disease is proof that too little is being done to protect the public from dangerous foods. So-called food experts are getting away with murder. They are never punished for their blatant errors and misinformation. Highly dangerous food has been allowed into our shops, and heads should roll for this latest disaster.

Activity ▷

- Find examples of the writer:
1 Using words to scare the reader.
2 Using words to shock the reader.
3 Using words that suggest there's no question about it.
4 Using words to exaggerate how bad things are.

The author of the next passage uses strong words to make schools sound like unhappy places:

I watched the grey children, shoulders stooped and feet dragging, shuffling their way towards a school that would be better described as a workhouse. How much happier they would be if their parents could educate them at home.

Activity ▷

- Find three ways the writer uses to make school sound like a miserable place.

Agent X-Libris

An article has appeared in the Cleator Moor newspaper about Mary Duke's time travel journey to the library. Turn to the story 'Time Slide' by Julia Jarman in *Stacks of Stories*. Your task is to seek out **bias** in the newspaper report.

GIRL IN LIBRARY RUMPUS

A female intruder was arrested by Constable Bull yesterday after disrupting the peace of the library and causing upset to the librarian.

Mary Duke, 9, burst into the library at 4.15pm wearing bizarre garments and shouting abuse and rude questions.

Unaware that children should be seen and not heard, she screeched across the library at the librarian Miss Clack, demanding answers to her frenzied questions.

Miss Clack was forced to restrain the girl, who was a menace to other library users. After a brief struggle, Miss Clack prevented further damage by escorting the defiant Mary Duke to the stock cupboard and locking the door.

'I had no alternative,' said Miss Clack later. 'I did it for the girl's own safety. She is obviously mad and needs help.'

Miss Clack then calmly called Constable Bull who punished the child for disturbing the peace.

Activity ▶▶

- Find examples of the way in which the article criticises Mary and favours Miss Clack.
- Compare Mary's account of the incident on pages 92–100 and find words used in the story to suggest that Mary was badly treated and scared. Useful pages are **95**, **96** and **99**.
- Write your own account of the incident for a different newspaper and aim to make the reader sympathise with Mary.

Language Workout

Bias

1 He reminds me of my own son! He's grown up and now he's a bank manager.

2 He's always getting blamed for things he didn't do. Just leave him alone!

3 It's all the result of TV! They see violence on TV and try to do the same.

4 He can't help upsetting our next door neighbour. I know he's a bit naughty but I think Mr Jones does go a bit over the top.

5 The trouble is when you get a bit older, you forget what it's like to be young.

6 Mr Jones hates all kids! He should stop moaning about everything and leave us all alone!

7 I blame the parents. They let their children run wild and this is the result.

8 I just don't know what to do with him.

9 He's mad! It's brilliant!

10 Mark gets into trouble, but don't most boys his age? There's no harm in Mark.

11 I just dread what he's going to do next! He's not a bad boy, but he just gets into so much trouble!

12 He's a little blighter. It's the same with all young people these days... they've no respect for their elders and betters!

Mark's mum

Mrs Higgins

Sally

Mr Jones

Activity ▷

Each person is saying three things about Mark but who is saying what? Match the name with the number of the speech bubble.

Jim Doolan is a biker. His mother loves him, but 17-year-old Sharon can't stand the noise he makes.

Activity ▷▷

Write two paragraphs – one for Sharon and one for Jim's mother – which describe Jim as each of them sees him. Do not write as 'I'. Start: 'Jim is...'

You are the Head of Year. Today you have to deal with a problem on the playing fields at lunchtime, where two groups were playing football.

Jason, a boy in Year 7, says he kicked his ball on to the Year 10 pitch by accident. When he went to collect it, a bigger boy kicked a ball into his face. His mates then bundled him off their pitch.

The Year 10 boy (Gary) says that the boy is always pestering them. He deliberately kicked his ball onto the pitch to disrupt their game. He was accidentally struck by a free kick. The Year 10 boys helped him off so that he could sit quietly and recover.

You will want to hear what the boys have to say.

List the words from the Word Bank that Year 7 Jason would use.

List the words from the Word Bank that Year 10 Gary would use.

Word Bank

bullies	accidentally	to safety	didn't see
ruined	dumped	ignored	picked on
helped	grabbed	jeering	no idea
pest	deliberately	smashed	spoilt

Activity ▶▶

- Now role play the interview in a group of five:
  1 The Head of Year   3 Jason's friend   5 Gary's friend
  2 Jason   4 Gary
- Let each person explain what happened.
  When you have heard each person's story, decide what you should do about it.

Fans

Arsenal 1 Manchester United 1

This was an exciting match, which could have gone either way. The United forwards were on top form, and Arsenal's defence were outstanding. United scored first, but there were appeals for offside. The referee allowed the goal. The Arsenal goal started as a long shot from mid-field. The shot bounced off a defender into the goal. The keeper had no chance.

But how did the Arsenal and the Manchester United fans describe it after the match?

Challenge

Design a quiz

Make up clues for a quiz to match these answers:

Questions must be six words long exactly.

Questions	Answers
Which a	adder
Which b	bear
Which c	coat
Which d	dance
Which e	engine
Which f	family
Which g	goldfish
Which h	headphones
Which i	ivy
Which j	jet
Which k	kitchen
Which l	library
Which m	microchip
Which n	newspaper
Which o	orange
Which p	penguin
Which q	queen
Which r	robber
Which s	scarf
Which t	town
Which u	unkind
Which v	vet
Which w	whale
Which x	xylophone
Which y	year
Which z	zebra

Well done!

Sentence Builder

Using commas

There are three main ways to use commas:

1 To separate items in a list.
2 To mark the change from the spoken part and the rest of the sentence.
3 Like brackets when you add an extra bit into a sentence, either in the middle or at the beginning.

Look at the commas in this passage and discuss with your partner where each kind of comma occurs.

> Mr Fox flattened his body against the ground and lay very still, his ears pricked. He waited a long time, but he heard nothing more.
>
> 'It must have been a field-mouse,' he told himself, 'or some other small animal.'
>
> He crept a little further out of the hole … then further still. He was almost right out in the open now. He took a last careful look around. The wood was murky and very still. Somewhere in the sky the moon was shining.
>
> Just then, his sharp night-eyes caught a glint of something bright behind a tree not far away. It was a small silver speck of moonlight shining on a polished surface. Mr Fox lay still, watching it. What on earth was it? Now it was moving. It was coming up and up … *Great heavens! It was the barrel of a gun!*

From *Fantastic Mr Fox* by Roald Dahl

Making sense

Find out how important commas are for meaning by circling each comma in the first paragraph on page 148 of *Stacks of Stories*, and putting a new comma one word later. Now try reading the passage, deliberately pausing one word after you should. For example.

'And soon not, (*pause*) only children...'

Activity ▶

Write a list of five things, using commas.

● You should have three commas. Why not four?

● Why do you think you need a comma between them?

Writing Workshop

Mini-story

This writer was challenged to write a story in less than 50 words. It had to be a story with a beginning, middle and an end. It could not be a simple description or an anecdote. It had to contain these three words: beach, bottle, message. She wrote the following story:

One summer I was walking along the beach, when I saw a bottle floating by with a message inside it. It was difficult to reach, because the waves carried it away, but I waded out to get it. The message read 'Who's got wet feet then?'

Although this is a mini-story, it still has shape:

- a beginning
- something happens
- things develop
- things come to a head.
- things come to an end

Activity

1 Choose any three of the words in the Word Bank.

2 Dream up a story using exactly 50 words and containing your three words. Write it on rough paper because it's hard to keep to 50 words. You might need to change it.

3 Cut out any useless words. Every word must pull its weight.

4 Improve any dull words. Think of a word that means the same thing but is more imaginative. Use a thesaurus to help you.

5 When your story is as good as it can be, write it out neatly.

Word Bank

pen	cafe
bag	bus
scarf	crocodile
letter	picnic
bee	feather
shoe	goat
tree	boy
car	shop
road	eagle
ice-cream	park

- Now try writing a mini-saga which is **exactly** 50 words – no more, no less. A mini-saga can have a title in addition. For example:

CHEERS! – A TRUE STORY

The small family wedding party was subdued. Beloved Grandma Ellen had died suddenly last month. The wine waiter brought champagne which no one had ordered.

'The lady rang us yesterday,' he said. 'She said you were to drink a toast and sent her love. Her name? – oh, yes, just Ellen.'

by REGINA MICHAEL

LIKE MOTHER, LIKE SON

1955
Dear Mummy,
I hate this boarding school. Food awful, prefects bully me. Please take me home.
Love,
        David

Dear David,
Nonsense! Chin up.
                Mother

1997
Dear David,
I hate this Home. Food awful, nurses treat me like a child. Fetch me immediately.
                Mother

Dear Mother,
Nonsense! Chin up.
                David

by PAULINE CARTLEDGE

Some possible titles:

- The lost letter
- Crossed wires
- The end of a beautiful friendship
- Strange meeting
- The last living…

Word Builder

Spelling check

Test yourself on the spellings from Unit Four by writing down:

A the 3 words which start a question

_____

_____

_____

C the 3 words about other people

_____

_____

_____

B the 3 words about place

_____

_____

_____

D the 3 words about listening

_____

_____

_____

Unit Five spellings

- Tick the words you can already spell.
- For others, use the matching colour to highlight the difficult part of the word, and find a way to remember the letters.

red	white	purple
yellow	black	silver
green	pink	gold
blue	orange	brown
grey		

Long E

There are four main ways of making the long E sound.

- EE   as in   p**ee**l
- EA   as in   p**ea**ch
- IE   as in   gr**ie**f
- E_E   as in   h**e**r**e**

Circle the parts of the following words that make the long E sound:

greet	reach	freedom	real	indeed
brief	between	succeed	reveal	relief
speak	reason	speech	team	these
grief	adhere	meaning	recede	believe
there	receive	belief	beach	beam

Help

1 Notice the words using IE. What do they have in common? (Think carefully about the origin of the word 'believe'.)

2 Words containing EE and EA often contain words within them. For example, FEELING contains FEE, EEL and FEEL. Can you find any in the other words?

Vocabulary: Defining words

- Imagine you are writing a dictionary.
- Try defining these words in exactly four words.

Fork is done for you.

Fork	*pronged*	*tool*	*for*	*eating*
Acorn				
Dog				
Biro				
Wheelbarrow				
Uncle				
Key				
Diamond				
Pen				
Train				

- Now try the same task with just two words:

Fork		
Acorn		
Dog		
Biro		
Wheelbarrow		
Uncle		
Key		
Diamond		
Pen		
Train		

- Now try the same task with just one word:

Fork	
Acorn	
Dog	
Biro	
Wheelbarrow	
Uncle	
Key	
Diamond	
Pen	
Train	

Make a crossword in the grid below.

Fit words in the gaps and work out some good clues.

Across

2 _____

4 _____

5 _____

7 _____

Down

1 _____

2 _____

3 _____

6 _____

Detective Reader

Taking a hint

Sometimes you know things without being told – you get the hint.

What sort of hints might tell you:

- that your friend is in a bad mood
- that someone fancies you
- that someone just read a letter containing bad news
- that the teacher is feeling frustrated.

In this passage from 'A Picture of Home' in *Stacks of Stories*, a girl tries to talk to her mother about the old days in Somalia, before they came to England. The story never tells us how the mother is feeling, but can you work it out?

That night, she told her mother about the computer picture. Her mother was getting the meal, and either she didn't want to make much of it, or she was too busy.

'That was then,' her mother said. 'This is now.'

Which made Ugaso go further. 'I sometimes dream that Dad is in the picture,' she told her.

'That is stupid! Dad was. We three are what there is now.' And with her pestle she pounded the rice as if it were an enemy.

It was the weekend, and, as if to poke Ugaso in the ribs with what she was trying to get her to understand, her mother spent the Saturday showing her which bus took them to the street market, and how to go to the post office to get money. And on the way home she said, 'Forget Dad' in the same matter-of-fact voice she'd used to buy the bus tickets.

Activity ▶

- Complete these starters:
  I think she is feeling…
  firstly, because of the way…
  secondly, because…
  and thirdly, because…

Help ▶▶

You might be able to guess how the mother is feeling by imagining how you would feel in the same position.

You might be able to find clues in the way she speaks.

You might find clues in the way she behaves.

Agent X-Libris

HQ want a young agent called Alice Brett to join our top secret Z-programme.

- Turn to the story 'Mozart's Banana' by Gillian Cross in the *Stacks of Stories* book. Find out what you can about Alice Brett's personality. You won't be told much, but you might be able to work it out.

- Write up your report using the boxes below as a guide. Good luck.

I learnt from the incident where Sammy Foster shows Alice his scar on pages 120–121 that Alice is

because

I learnt from the incidents at the library van on pages 121–124 that Alice is

because

I learnt from the incident where Alice leaves the sick room on pages 126–127 that Alice is

because

I learnt from the incident where Alice falls off the horse on pages 132–133 that Alice is

because

- Write a section of a school report for Alice Brett, explaining her personal qualities.

Language Workout

Tact

Usually people mean what they say. But not always.

- Look carefully at the following. Which characters mean what they say? And if some of them don't mean what they say, what do they mean?

Every morning, Michael wakes his sister Karen with a wet flannel.

Brian's PE teacher has told him he can be reserve goalkeeper in the third team.

Brian's PE teacher has arranged a trial with Manchester United.

Lianne always shares her mother's cooking with her dog under the table.

Activity ▷

- Can you think of situations where you have tried to be tactful?
- When should people be tactful instead of truthful?

A tactful letter

Dean has been on holiday with his rich Aunt Jean at the seaside. He has not enjoyed himself. Now he has a problem. He always sends his aunt a thank-you letter and when he does she sends him a postal order for £20. This is the letter he has written so far. Read it carefully and work out what really happened on the holiday.

11th November

Dear Aunt Jean,

Thank you for inviting me on holiday. I really enjoyed the four-mile walk to the nearest shop as it helped me keep fit. It was fun having to cross the field full of black bulls as I have always been interested in wildlife. It was great too that it rained every day, as I really enjoyed watching the rainbows from my room.

Activity ▶

Complete the letter. There are several points that you have to cover in the most tactful way you can:

- a lumpy bed in which you could hardly sleep
- eating piles of cooked vegetables instead of your usual hamburgers and chips
- the dog, which chewed great chunks out of your trousers
- listening to Uncle Raymond's boring little talks about birds
- watching the slides of Aunt Jean and Uncle Raymond's holiday in Skegness instead of watching cable television
- you won't be able to go next year as you're going to Disneyland instead.

When you have finished your letter, share it with a partner. The partner's job is to read it from the point of view of Aunt Jean. Does it cover all the points? And does it cover the points in a tactful way? Decide whether it deserves the £20 postal order.

After the party

You organised a birthday party for your little brother when your mum was in hospital. Everything that could have gone wrong did. Make a list of all the things that went wrong.

Activity ▶▶

Now you have to phone your mum to reassure her that everything went well. You must mention all the bad points, but tell them in a way that won't stress her. Think very carefully how you are going to do this. Make a few notes in the right-hand column to help you say it tactfully.

- Make that phone call. Record it if you have a tape recorder.

Help ▶▶

Here are some ideas to get you started:

- Coca Cola was flat
- grumpy family next door meant that you had to keep the music down
- no candles for the birthday cake
- gatecrashers arrived and pulled a sink off the wall.

Challenge

Criss cross words

This game is played like noughts and crosses, but the aim is to spell words. Use two different coloured pens and take turns to fill in a letter. When you complete a three-letter word, put a line through it and carry on. Words can go up, down, back, forward or diagonally in a straight line.

For example:

P	U	C
A	I	O
N	U	G

Jasmine made two words:

cog   pig

Stephen made four words:

pan   nap   gun   cup

score box

score box

score box

score box

Now try it with 16 boxes, making three or four letter words.

Sentence Builder

Making and breaking sentences

Activity ▶▶

- Read the following sentence from 'Small World' on page 61 of *Stacks of Stories*.

Nothing of him showed above the table but the tuft of hair which always stuck up because his mother saved money by cutting it herself.

- Write out the sentence and then use a pen to break it down into three separate sentences.
- Can you join them back up together in a different way?
- What methods can you use to link small sentences together?

Dropping in extra information

Activity ▶▶

Read this from 'Small World':

Ralph, who was on holiday, went to Venice, which is the sinking city.

Bill, who had no money, went to the library, which was just down the street.

Extra information has been added to two basic sentences.

- Try deleting the extra bits to find the basic sentences.
- What are the two tell-tale signs that extra bits have been added?

Writing Workshop

Shock Horror Headlines

HUMPTY IN DEATH PLUNGE

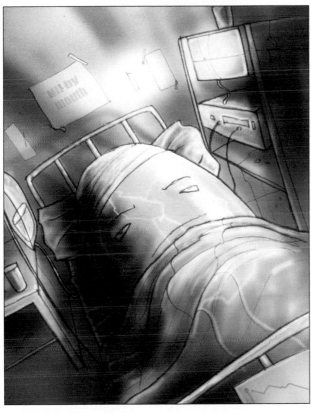

Humpty Dumpty fell from a 40 foot wall today. The King's Horses and Men who were in the area tried to put the badly injured egg-man Humpty back together, but could not. He was taken to Wallsend Hospital but doctors said he was dead on arrival. Was it a tragic accident – or did he fall, or worse, was he pushed?

COW IN ORBIT

Experts last night were trying to work out the biggest space mystery ever. How did a cow get into outer space? And when it reached the moon how did it jump over? Possible links are being made with the strange theft of a spoon back on Earth. Last night a corgi called Rex was helping police with their enquiries.

Activity ▷▷

1 Write amusing headlines for three more fairytales or nursery rhymes. Choose the best one and retell it so you remember what is in it. You are going to write a newspaper article about it.

2 Pick out the bit of the story that would catch the imagination of the reader and write the opening sentence of the article. For example:

> *The Pigg Brothers of Windy Lane were left homeless last night as local builder, B.B. Wolf destroyed their home in a bizarre act of vandalism.*

3 Start a new paragraph with a sentence which explains in exciting language what happened. For example:

> *Onlookers were astonished when B.B. Wolf launched a hurricane-force attack on the new straw house of the youngest Pigg brother.*

4 In another sentence explain what led up to it. For example:

> *The act is the result of a long-running feud between the brothers and the local builder who had been threatening for months to huff and puff and blow their house down.*

5 In another sentence, tell the reader what the immediate result was. For example:

> *The recently built straw house of the younger brother was completely destroyed in the attack.*

6 Start a new paragraph to interview one of the characters. Put the spoken words inside speech marks and remember to start with a capital letter. For example:

> *'We're not defeated,' said the middle Pigg last night. 'Today we start work on a house made of sticks. He can huff and puff all he likes but he won't blow that house down in a hurry!'*

7 In the last paragraph, tell the reader what will happen as a result and tell readers what they can do to help. For example:

> *Police are appealing for eye witnesses to help them with their enquiries. They are warning members of the public to keep away from B.B. Wolf. Sightings of B.B. Wolf should be reported to the incident room on 01235 678952 with information.*

8 Write your headline and article on a computer then print it out.

Word Builder

Spelling check

Test yourself on the spellings from Unit Five, which were thirteen colours.

r _____   y _____

g _____   b _____

w _____   b _____

p _____   o _____

p _____   s _____

g _____   b _____

g _____

Unit Six spellings

Colour in the silent letter in these much-used words.

A good way to remember silent letters is to pronounce them when you say the word aloud. It's funny – but it works.

know   knife

library   wreck

muscle   thumb

write   rhyme

Long I

There are three main ways of making the long I sound:

- I_E   as in   TIME
- Y   as in   ST**Y**
- IGH   as in   S**IGH**T

Most words use **I_E**.

Activity ⯈

Only three four-letter words end in IGH.

Think hard and then write them down in your workbook:

	i	g	h

	i	g	h

	i	g	h

Activity ⯈

Many more words end in 'IGHT'. How many words can you make by connecting the letters outside the circle to the 'IGHT' in the circle? List them in your workbook.

s l r f r n l p l s t f l e c r a
g r c d r p d s t g m b b l f a

IGHT

Some common long I words end in Y. For example:

m**y**   st**y**

- Can you think of eight more?
- Do you notice any patterns?

Vocabulary

Within the last 100 years, someone has had to invent new words for new things such as:

- megabyte
- microchip
- mini-skirt
- pop star
- hamburger

- Euro
- hovercraft
- helicopter
- floppy disk
- television

These things simply didn't exist 100 years ago.

Can you think of any others, and work out how they were chosen?

Activity ▶

Make up some new words. What could you call the following:

- The metal thing that closes a zip?
- Hard chewing gum stuck underneath the desk?
- The noise that chairs make when you push them back?
- That restless feeling you get when you hear the class next door packing up?
- TVs and video machines that never work when you need them?

Think up some more useful words for school.

Detective Reader

Character study

Characters in books are not real people. They are made up of descriptions, speeches and accounts. They are like portraits, but made out of words.

It is important to understand characters and to feel for them. If you do, you will become involved and interested in the story. Read this extract about a boy called Spit Nolan:

What do the circled words tell you about Spit Nolan's health?

List the words that tell you something about his personality.

List the words that hint at his life, family and background.

> Spit Nolan was a pal of mine. He was a (thin) lad with a (bony face) that was always (pale) except for two (rosy spots) on his cheekbones. He had quick brown eyes, short, wiry hair, rather stooped shoulders, and we all knew that he only had one lung. **He had a disease which in those days couldn't be cured unless you went away to Switzerland, which Spit certainly couldn't afford.** He wasn't sorry for himself in any way, and in fact we envied him, because he never had to go to school.
>
> Spit was the champion trolley-rider of Cotton-Pocket; that was the district in which we lived. He had a very good balance and sharp wits, and he was very brave, so that these qualities, when added to his skill as a rider, meant that no other boy could ever beat Spit on a trolley – and every lad had one.

List the words that describe Spit's appearance.

Do you know which disease this is and what causes it?

List the words that describe Spit Nolan's skills.

Activity ▶

You should now have a long list of words that describe Spit Nolan's appearance.

- Draw a picture of him.
- Around your picture, write some words to sum up his personality. These can be your own words.
- Then, in a different colour, write some words describing his skills.
- Finally, in another colour, write some words about his life, family and background.

Agent X-Libris

Department S believe that some people are turning themselves into books and entering some kind of library heaven. Find out if a character called Mr Fogbeam in 'Were-books' by Douglas Hill in the *Stacks of Stories* book is a suitable person to join this library heaven. Report back your answer with evidence in a table similar to the one below. That's your mission. Good luck.

Personal Qualities	Evidence

I can/cannot recommend Mr Fogbeam for a 'library heaven' for these reasons:

1

2

4

5

To do well in tests, remember:

- to provide evidence for your answers
- to give a handful of answers, or angles on the answer.

Language Workout

Pen portraits

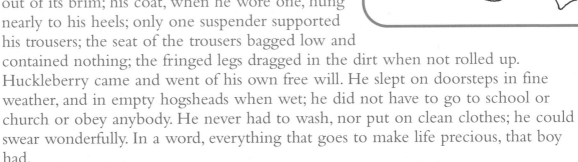

Huckleberry Finn

Huckleberry Finn was a country boy living in America more than a hundred years ago.

Huckleberry was always dressed in the cast off clothes of full grown men, fluttering with rags. His hat was a ruin with a wide crescent lopped out of its brim; his coat, when he wore one, hung nearly to his heels; only one suspender supported his trousers; the seat of the trousers bagged low and contained nothing; the fringed legs dragged in the dirt when not rolled up. Huckleberry came and went of his own free will. He slept on doorsteps in fine weather, and in empty hogsheads when wet; he did not have to go to school or church or obey anybody. He never had to wash, nor put on clean clothes; he could swear wonderfully. In a word, everything that goes to make life precious, that boy had.

From *The Adventures of Huckleberry Finn* **by Mark Twain**

Scrooge

Scrooge is an old and mean Victorian businessman.

Scrooge! A squeezing, wrenching, grasping, scraping, clutching old sinner! Hard and sharp as a flint, secret and self contained and solitary. The cold within him froze his old features, nipped his pointed nose, shrivelled his cheek and made his eyes red, his thin lips blue and spoke out shrewdly in his grating voice.

Nobody ever stopped him in the street to say, 'My dear Scrooge, how are you?' No beggars implored him to give a little. Even the blind men's dogs appeared to know him; and when they saw him coming on, they would tug their owners into doorways.

From *A Christmas Carol* **by Charles Dickens**

Mr and Mrs Gargery

Mr and Mrs Gargery are a Victorian couple.

My sister, Mrs Joe Gargery, was more than twenty years older than I, and had a great reputation because she had brought me up 'by hand'. Having at that time to find out what the expression meant, and knowing her to have a hard and heavy hand, and to be much in the habit of laying it upon her husband as well as upon me, I supposed that Joe Gargery and I were both brought up by hand.

She was not a good-looking woman, my sister; and I had a general impression she must have made Joe Gargery marry her by hand. Joe was a fair man, with curls of flaxen hair on each side of his smooth face, and with eyes of such blue that they seemed to have got mixed up with their own whites. He was a mild, good-natured, sweet-tempered, foolish, dear fellow – a sort of Hercules in strength and in weakness.

My sister, Mrs Joe, with black hair and eyes, had such a prevailing redness of skin that I sometimes used to wonder whether it was possible she washed herself with a nutmeg-grater instead of soap. She was tall and bony, and almost always wore a coarse apron with a square bib in front that was stuck full of pins and needles.

From *Great Expectations* by Charles Dickens

Activity ▷

Look carefully at the way each of the four characters is described.

- Underline the words and phrases that describe the appearance of each character.

- Then fill in the pictures of each character. Include as many details from the writing as you can.

- Next, in a different colour, highlight the words which tell you about their personalities.

Activity

Now create a character of your own.

- Make notes about your character in the space provided.
  Include as many details as you can, so the picture will be easy to draw.

- Write up a full description on a separate piece of paper and pass your book to a partner. Your partner has to sketch and label the character, based on your description.

Help

Characters you could use:

- a very strict teacher
- a cheerful dinner lady
- a spoilt and selfish little girl.

My character:

Details of appearance:

1 _____
2 _____
3 _____
4 _____
5 _____
6 _____

Details of personality:

1 _____
2 _____
3 _____

Sketch Box

Role Play

- Pick a character and write down three key words to describe him or her, for example, **fussy**.

- In role, act like the character and talk about things that you have done today.

- Other members of the group have to describe what kind of person you are playing. See if they can guess your three key words.

Challenge

Words within words

How many words can be found within the word VEGETABLE?

No jumbled words allowed. No names allowed.

You should find: GET   TAB   TABLE   ABLE

Now try the activity – remember, no jumbled words or names allowed.

Activity ▶

1 Can you find six words in FIRELIGHTER?
2 Can you find seven words in TOGETHER?
3 Can you find six words in PHOTOGRAPHY?
4 How many words can you find in GRANDMOTHER?
5 How many words can you find in your own name?
   Who in the class has the most?
6 List any words you can find with three or more words in them.
   The winner is the one who gets the most.

How many words can you think of that contain the word SIGN?

You should find: SIGNAL   SIGNATURE   ASSIGNMENT

Now try the activity.

Activity ▶

1 How many words can you think of that contain the word POST?
2 How many words can you think of that contain the word GRAM?
3 How many words can you think of that contain the word DRESS?
4 How many words can you think of that contain the word SIDE?
5 How many words can you think of that contain the word SCRIPT?

Sentence Builder

Stripping back sentences

Three sentences from 'Small World' in the *Stacks of Stories* book have been taken apart and jumbled up.

Onto the table went every book

They spent hours together

numberless as ants

on the next country

The librarians put a table for him out of the way

in the bay marked local history

marvelling over photographs of workers

where the public rarely intruded.

in Bill's world tour.

the Library could offer

swarming up and down mountains of mud.

Activity ▶▶

1 Copy the lines and tick the ones that could make sense on their own. These are **clauses**. They read like very simple sentences. (The others are **phrases** – they don't make sense on their own.)

2 Cut all the pieces up and put them in order.

3 Check your order on page 67 of *Stacks of Stories*.

4 Take away the **phrases**. You can do without them if you need to. They are the tack-on bits that would not make sense on their own.

5 Can you think of a way to join up the three remaining clauses into one sentence?

6 Read the opening of 'Small World' up to 'Neat did not cover it' on page 60. Use your red pen to edit out those bits you don't need. Read it through aloud to check it makes sense.

Writing Workshop

Starting your story

You will now start to write a long story. This story has no title yet – you will choose a title after you have written the whole story. In this unit, your aim is to write an interesting opening.

An interesting start

It is a cold, dull Saturday. You and two friends have no pocket money so you decide to cycle to a local wood and spend a few hours having fun. Your two friends overtake you and disappear round a bend. A few minutes later you turn the corner only to find both bikes lying on the ground, the front wheel of one of the bikes still spinning...

You notice a cave and walk towards it...

Activity ▷▷

Begin your story as all three of you are cycling through the wood.

- In the first paragraph, set the scene for a chilling mystery. Get the reader in the right mood. Put in some worrying details.

  Remember to introduce your friends.

- Start like this: 'It was a cold, dull Saturday as we headed into...'. End where your friends disappear round the bend. Write no more than about 10–12 lines.

- Start the next paragraph as you round the corner.

  Describe what you see, including the bike's wheel still spinning. Also describe the silence.

- Now add the third paragraph by writing about your thoughts and feelings at that very moment.

Word Builder

Spelling check

Test yourself on the spellings from Unit Six, which contain silent letters.

The teacher will read out the words.

1 _____   6 _____

2 _____   7 _____

3 _____   8 _____

4 _____   9 _____

5 _____   10 _____

Unit Seven spellings

Today's spellings are words for your timetable.

English   Technology
Science   Biology
Chemistry   Physics
History   Assembly
Drama   French
German   Mathematics
Geography

- Your teacher will add any others you need.
- Connect words with lines and colour in the parts that have the same groups of letters. For example: **'y'   'ology'**
- Tick off the ones you know and concentrate on the ones you get wrong.

Long O

There are three main ways of making a long O sound:

O_E   as in B**O**N**E**

OA   as in B**OA**T

OW   as in GR**OW**

Write down eight words **starting** with a long O.

Write down eight words **ending** in a long O.

Write down eight words with a long O **in the middle**.

- Can you see any patterns?
- Did you find any other ways of spelling a long O?
- Can you think of any words in which O_E, OA or OW don't make a long O sound? Give examples.

Vocabulary: school subjects

- Choose five words from your school subject spelling list. Try to make as many new words from your five words as possible. You have to use letters in the word in the correct order.

Score 1 mark for each word using 3 letters.
Score 2 marks for each word using 4 letters.
Score 3 marks for each word using 5 letters.

For example:

FRENCH

fresh	1		trench	3
rent	1		pence	1
bench	2			

Score = 8 points

Detective Reader

Working out why people do what they do

Why do people act the way they do? Very often, they have a motive – a reason for doing it.

In this passage a young girl wants to sail in a fishing boat to a dangerous beach in France to rescue some trapped soldiers.

> British soldiers were trapped there, they said. Thousands and thousands. And so were the French. The Germans and their tanks would capture them. Families would lose all those men who were uncles and brothers and fathers and sons. Every boat on the English coast was needed to go and help. The owners were to report for orders, and for maps, and charts. My brother John was a British soldier, fighting in France.

The Little Ships by **Louise Borden**

- Find four possible motives why the girl might risk her life taking a boat to rescue soldiers on the beach.

In this passage a Chinese boy, Tien Pao, is desperate to board a packed train to escape enemy soldiers. He is saved by a stranger. Why? What could be the motive?

- What possible motives could the soldier have for saving the boy?
- Which is the most likely motive and why?
- What clues are there in the language?

> It was hopeless. The freight car was as packed as the passenger train. Even the wide doorway was solid with people. They teetered on the edge. Tien Pao clung to the wheel to keep himself from being crushed. Hopelessly he looked up at the high doorway. For a moment a tall soldier looked down into his eyes. Suddenly he stooped, his long arm shot out; he grabbed Tien Pao's collar and lifted him into the car like a drowned puppy.

The House of Sixty Fathers by **Meindert DeJong**

Agent X-Libris

Proceed to Crimmond library in 'Small World' by Geraldine McCaughrean in the *Stacks of Stories* book. Your task is to find out why the grown-ups have been behaving strangely. Find out how they are helping the boy and why they are doing it.

Activity ⏵⏵

Copy and fill in this table. The page references will help you. There's no need to read every word. Find the relevant bits and use them.

Character	Pages	How they helped Bill	Why they helped Bill
Mrs Hattersley	62 63–64 67	She helped Bill by	She helped because I know this because it says
Mrs Copple	69–70	She helped Bill by	She helped because I know this because it says
Mr Lane	64 68–69 71	He helped Bill by	He helped because I know this because it says
Oriole Wynne and the Librarians	67 70	They helped Bill by	They helped because I know this because it says

Language Workout

Superglue

Read the story:

No one ever forgot the hot summer day in the last week of term when class 6G arrived at school to find all the doors had been superglued shut. No one could get in, not even the Head teacher Mrs Potts.

Tina Watts giggled to her friend Tracey Bagley: 'Oh good. Now we can't have that spelling test with Mrs O'Leary!'

'What do you mean?' replied Tracey. 'I only needed one more credit for a Gold award. I'd have got full marks, I know I would. Now I won't get a chance!'

The first person to get blamed was Brian O'Toole, for the simple reason he had glue on his hands. But Brian was quick to explain that he had been making a model aeroplane at home. And everyone knew how keen he was on his hobby.

'Come on, Brian!' shouted Tina Watts. 'Everyone knows you like playing practical jokes. Admit you did it!'

'I would admit, if I had done it,' said Brian calmly, 'but it just so happens that I didn't.'

It took at least an hour for the locksmith to arrive. For some reason Mr Jolly, our form teacher, had not arrived. This was unusual, as Mr Jolly was never away.

'I hope he's alright,' said Tina. 'He's got all our money for the French trip. Today's the last day for paying in.'

'Actually,' said Brian, 'I remember now. I saw a car at the school on Saturday night. It looked like Mr Jolly's old Metro.'

'Oh don't be ridiculous, Brian!' said Mrs Potts. 'Mr Jolly is always coming in, for one reason or another.' But for the first time, she did not sound so sure.

Having read the first part of the story, write down who you think might have done it? Give reasons for your choices.

Now read on:

Suddenly a car came speeding through the school gates. It came to a halt in a cloud of dust and out stepped – Mr Jolly.

'Sorry I'm late everyone,' he announced. 'Some silly idiot thought it was clever to superglue the doors of my car!'

'Superglue!' Mrs Potts gave a sharp intake of breath. 'What on earth's going on?'

But before anyone could say anything else, another vehicle sped through the gates. This time it was a white van with J. Booker, Locksmith written on the side.

'I'm having a busy morning!' announced Mr Booker as he stepped out with his tool bag. 'Business is looking up!'

'Shouldn't we wait for the police?' asked Mr Jolly, standing in front of the main door.

'What's the point?' said Mr Booker frowning. 'Do you want to get into the school or don't you? I can't wait about all day.'

'Oh let's just get in!' said Tracey Bagley.

'We will wait for the police,' announced Mrs Potts. 'There could be fingerprints and that could lead us to the culprit!'

'Dream on,' muttered Tracey under her breath.

Activity ▷▷

Having read the second part of the story, who do you think did it? Complete the following sentences in your workbook. Make sure that you give reasons for your choices.

- I think that _____ did it, because _____ .

- I think that _____ might have done it, because

  _____ .

- I think that _____ did not do it, because _____ .

Now read on:

It took another hour for the police to turn up. They dusted the doors for fingerprints, which was fun. Then Mr Booker, who had decided to wait, drilled the locks from the doors.

Mr Jolly went straight to the safe, where the money for the French trip was kept. After a moment he brought out a large brown envelope – nothing was missing.

Tina took no notice. Instead she turned to Brian O'Toole.

'What I don't understand, Brian, is why you said you saw Mr Jolly's car outside the school on Saturday night.'

Brian sighed deeply. 'I said it, Tina, because I did see it.'

'But you were out on Saturday night, Brian, because I saw you at the cinema. You didn't see me because I was four rows back, but I did see you!'

'I was at home on Saturday,' insisted Brian, 'and I had no money for the cinema.' But he was breathing heavily, and a flush appeared on his cheeks.

'Funny you were buying sweets on Sunday at the shop, Brian,' chipped in Tracey, 'if you had nop money!'

Brian spoke through gritted teeth. 'I had no reason to glue up the school! And you're just saying that Tracey, because I saw you chatting with the locksmith. How much did he give you?'

There was a sudden hush. All eyes turned to Tracey. 'He … he's a friend of the family,' she stammered. 'I've known him since I was six!'

Role Play

Inspector Wordsworth is called in to interview anyone who might be connected with the supergluing of the school.

- In groups of six take one part each:
  - Inspector Wordsworth
  - Mr Jolly
  - Brian O'Toole
  - Tina Watts
  - Tracey Bagley
- Role-play the interviews. The sixth member of the group decides who is guilty.

Activity ▶

Having read the final part of the story, who do you think did it? Once again, give reasons for your choices.

Challenge

Call my bluff

You will need a dictionary. Work in threes.

Activity ▷▷

1 Use a big dictionary and find an unusual word, which no one has heard of, for example, **grison**.

2 Write down its true **meaning**.

3 Now make up two other possible meanings and write them down. Lay it out like this:

> A grison: a very old person who has spent a long time in prison.
>
> B grison: a small, bitter apple.
>
> C grison: a weasel-like mammal with dark fur and a white stripe across its forehead.

Each person in the group takes responsibility for one of the definitions.

4 The first group writes its word on the board, then in turn the people in the group have to persuade the class that their definition is the true one.

5 Other groups must now decide which definition they believe and write down A, B, or C.

6 The person who gave the true definition holds up their hand. All those who voted for it get a point.

7 Now each of the other groups take a turn and the winner is the group with most points for correct guesses.

Sentence Builder

Editing down

Sometimes you have to shorten writing because it's too long, too boring or won't fit. The simplest way of doing this is to cross things out because:

1 They're not important.

2 The basic point has been made already.

Activity ▶▶

- Try cutting out about half of the following passage but make sure that it still makes sense and that all the important bits are still in. You can cross out words, phrases or even whole sentences. You can add in the odd useful word if you need to.

I first saw the ghost outside my sleep-room window one evening as it was getting dark. He wasn't obviously a ghost, not semi-transparent, or glowing or anything. He just looked like an ordinary man, not old but not young, nothing unusual apart from the old-fashioned clothes he wore. And he had nothing on his head, so I could see his face clearly.

It was more his behaviour that was peculiar. He was carrying something under his arm – I couldn't make out what – and he came up to the window and sort of squashed his nose up against it, looking in, as if he couldn't see me. And then he vanished.

I don't mean that I turned my light on and couldn't see him any more, or that he moved quickly away. He just disappeared – there one minute and gone the next, like a wiped computer file.

From *How to Live Forever* by Mary Hoffman

- Now try cutting it down by half again. What do you have left? Compare it with other people's. How did you decide what to cut out?

  Try this again with the passage on page 76 of *Stacks of Stories* which begins 'And now Mr Fogbeam...' and ends: '...and his dreaming'.

Writing Workshop

Building up tension

The story continues as you enter the cave. Your aim today is to build up a creepy atmosphere as you walk through the cave. You see a blue light ahead and you think you can hear some muffled voices. As you journey through the cave the voices get louder…

Help ▶

- Close your eyes and imagine yourself entering the cave. Imagine walking through it.
- Think about what you HEAR, what you SEE, what you TOUCH, what you SMELL, even what you TASTE.

Activity ▶

Now write.

Start: I hastily dropped my own bike to the ground and walked to the mouth of the cave. I hesitated for a moment then stepped inside…

End with: I could still hear the muffled voices but could not understand what they were saying.

Word Builder

Spelling check

Test yourself on the spellings from Unit Seven, which were words for your new timetable. The teacher will remind you.

1 _____   6 _____

2 _____   7 _____

3 _____   8 _____

4 _____   9 _____

5 _____   10 _____

Plus any other subjects special to your school.

Unit Eight spellings

Write here ten spellings which always give you trouble.

Check the spellings are correct in a dictionary.

Tricky word	Best way to learn it

Help ▶▶

Think of a way to learn each new spelling. Will any of these ideas help you?

1 Say the word out loud very slowly to hear the sounds in order.

2 Break the word into syllables and spell each bit.

3 Say it out loud, even the silent letters, so you can hear it all.

4 Use a memory trick. For example:
- necessary = one **c**ollar, two **s**leeves
- because = **b**ig **e**lephants **c**an **a**lways **u**se **s**ome **e**ggs.

5 Find words inside it. For example:
- there's a **rat** in sep**arat**e.

6 Circle, highlight or underline the hard part – think of a way to remember it.

7 Think of family words, such as:
- light, sight, right
- definite, finite, infinity (you can hear the 'i' more clearly).

necessary

1 collar

2 sleeves

Long U sound

There are three main ways of making the long U sound:

U_E   as in   T**UBE**

OO   as in   B**OO**T

EW   as in   CH**EW**

Write out the words below with the correct long U spelling:

Activity ▷

Dr_ _

Ch_ _se

F_ _ _

N_ _ _

F_ _d

T_ _l

P_ _r_

R_ _d_

St_ _ _

M_ _ _n

M_ l_

R_ _ _t

L_ _ _se

Gr_ _ _

Activity ▷

- Where in a word are you most likely to find U_E, OO and EW?
- Read the list aloud and listen for one way of writing long U which sounds slightly different from the others. Which one sounds different and why?
- Make up a sentence containing as many EW sounds as possible.
- Can you think of words containing a long U sound but spelt differently? (There are not so many of these.)
  - something to eat
  - fighting families
  - a board game
  - a soldier
  - a holiday trip.

Vocabulary: Comparatives and superlatives

Activity ▶▶

Think of six words which might describe a person.
For example, **noisy**, **tall**. Copy out the table below and list them in the left-hand column.

Adjective	Comparative	Superlative
Tall	Taller	Tallest

- Compare yourself with people in the class using the adjectives you have just written in the left-hand column. For example:
  – I am **taller** than John.
  – I am the **neatest** writer.

- How do you add to or change the word to say someone is **more or better than** you?

- How do you add to or change the word to say someone is the **most or best at** something?

  You should find at least two answers to each question.
  Now fill in the middle and right-hand columns of your table.

- What are the comparatives and superlatives for:
  bad   **good**   **little**   **much**?

Detective Reader

What kind of story is it?

Activity ▷▷

There are many different types of story such as horror stories or detective stories.

Make a list of different types and write down an example for each one.

Type of Story	Example
Detective story	Sherlock Holmes

In which type of story would you expect to find each of the following?

Robots
Shoot-outs in the dark
Unexplained deaths
Dancing
Churchyards
Travel to other planets
Start by finding a dead body
Dinner parties

Monsters
A mad scientist
Heartbreak
Being scared
Chases
Lots of blood
Beautiful young women
Beautiful women spies

Strange noises in the night
Candlelight
Dashing heroes
Long slow kisses
Narrow escapes
Castles
Foreign travel

Activity ▷▷

In a group, choose one particular type of story and say what kind of characters, events, settings and language you expect to find.

You can tell what type of story you are reading because it might have:

- typical characters
- special language
- a familiar storyline.

This is obviously a fairy tale. But how do you know?

One day a poor pedlar sat beside his sick son. The boy was pale and feverish and could barely open his lips to sip water or eat bread. Just then there was a knock on the wooden door to his cottage. He opened the door. There stood an old hag. In one hand she held a basket and in the other a silver cord. At the end of the cord was a golden eagle.

Activity ▷▷

Can you spot any
- typical characters?
- telltale language?
- typical events or situations?

What type of story is this taken from and how do you know?

The footprints were clear to see in the soft mud. Each one had the X that she had secretly carved in the soles of the man's shoes clear for all to see. They led to the old barn. Beside them was a fine gold dust which must have leaked out from the tiny hole Dolly had made in the stolen sack.

'This should be all the evidence we need,' said Dolly in a whisper. 'Ben should be here with the police any minute now.' It was then that they heard a branch crack behind them.

Activity ▷▷

If you know what kind of story it is, you might be able to guess how it will continue. Discuss this then turn to page 120 for the original storyline. How close was your guess?

What kind of story are these two snippets taken from and how do you know?

The round metal shapes poured down to earth from the now, orange sky. When they had all landed we saw that they were the size of small houses and a green mist surrounded each one. There was a soft hum. As we all stared in silence, the space pods began to open.

As the dark shapes surged towards the Tree of Logres, he knew it was up to him. This was the reason he had been brought here. He was the only one who could stop the darkness. He must call on the powers the old wizard had shown him.

Activity ▷▷

Choose either one of these two passages.
Predict what will happen next, and write the next paragraph in the same style.

Agent X-Libris

'How to Live Forever' by Mary Hoffman in the *Stacks of Stories* book could go in the ghost or the science fiction section of a library. Make a case for each using the template below to help you.

Activity ▷

It should go in the **science fiction** section because it says on page:

106	
108	
109	
110	

Find three reasons to put the story in the **ghost section**:

1 _____

_____

_____

2 _____

_____

_____

3 _____

_____

_____

Language Workout

Give us a clue

Book covers grab your attention. They also tell you what sort of story you are going to read. Look at these four covers and predict what each story will be about. What makes you think so?

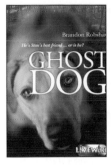 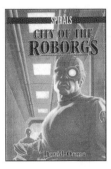 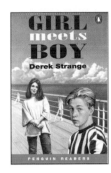 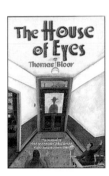

On the back of each book is a 'blurb' to tell you about the story and get you interested in it. Which blurb goes with which cover?

A

Stan's best friend is his dog, Rex. They are never apart. That is, until the day Stan is involved in a train crash, and has to stay in hospital. Can Stan ever forgive himself for what happens to Rex? One year on, the memory still haunts him...

B

Donna sees Mark on the boat to Spain. She likes him and he likes her. Then Mark sees Donna dancing with his brother, Dave... Is Donna in love with Mark? Why is Dave dancing with her?

C

Mina Ransom's uncle is a powerful man. He controls the city using terrifying half-human, half robot creatures made from the bodies of human 'trouble-makers'.

D

Maddie and her brother, Keith, have no memory of their father. He has been 'away on business' since before Keith was born. So when a charming stranger arrives, claiming to be their dad, both children try hard to welcome him enthusiastically. But things aren't quite right. Their home no longer feels their own. It's as though their every move is being watched. Who is he really? And what does he want?

- Write down all the hints and clues that helped you to match up the covers and blurbs. How many depend on you already knowing something about the way particular stories work?

- Now look at the opening lines of the four novels. Can you tell which goes with which? What clues can you find?

A

It's a funny thing, darkness.

Sometimes it can be comforting. Like the darkness under the covers when you were a kid, when you pulled your blanket cover over your head to hide from the ghosts and vampires you imagined were waiting to pounce.

Sometimes it can be frightening. Like the darkness in the basement of the old house you used to live in, where it was inky black – even in daytime.

And sometimes it can be lonely. Like the darkness you face near midnight, as you drive the deserted roads on the outskirts of town, wondering where it had all gone wrong.

B

No moon or stars were reflected in the surface of the water. Night lay heavy on the river. But in the distance, some miles upstream, an unhealthy glow stained the sky a dirty orange: the lights of Pridebridge Town.

A large boat lay moored at the bank. Light spilled from the galley porthole close to the stern.

In the galley, Maddie sat down heavily, causing *The Pridebridge Princess* to rock from side to side. Dark water slopped against the hull of Grandad Lemon's riverboat. Maddie turned her large face to stare at the old man. His question had taken her by surprise.

C

In the middle of the night, he woke up. He heard a noise. It was a dog scratching at his bedroom door. Whining to be let in.

A chill of fear ran through him. He pulled the covers over his head. He lay in bed, stiff and still. He prayed that the whining and scratching would stop. It didn't stop. It went on and on.

D

My story starts in late July. It was July 21st, I think. It was the first day of our holiday, a hot July day. I stood in the sun and looked at the sea. It was eleven o'clock in the morning. I was on the boat at Portsmouth with my mother and father and my sister, Louise. Sea birds played near our big boat and the small boats near us on the sea.

I started to look at the people with us on our boat... They were all happy on the first day of their holiday too. And suddenly there he was, this tall, quiet boy in a blue and white shirt; he was really good-looking. I'll always remember the first time I saw him.

Activity

- Each of the books fits into one of these genres or types of story:

  Science fiction   **Horror**   **Crime thriller**   **Romance**

- Decide which one is which.

- Write out some words and phrases that are typical of that type of story.

Challenge

Hidden words

Each group of letters conceals TWO WORDS. These words read from left to right and the letters are in the correct order.

For example:

S H H E O E R P S E = SHEEP HORSE

Activity ⟩

When you have found one whole word, write it down, then cross out or highlight the letters. This will help you find the second one faster. The clues might help you.

Words		Clues
C T H A A B I L R E	=	furniture
W H T E H R E E R E	=	places
P A E P A P C L H E	=	fruits
S O B O L U G D H T	=	trade
D P U R I N C K E E	=	royalty
E F I G H O T R T Y	=	numbers
S C O M T O R I C Y	=	something to read
V H I O A L R I P N	=	musical instruments
R I W G R O H N T G	=	judgements
T E P E A O P M L E	=	group

- In pairs, think of five words that you find hard to spell. Check the spellings and write them down.
- Find another word linked to each one by meaning, and about the same length.
- Mix the two words and write a clue.
- Swap with another team. The winner is the team who finishes first and has spelt the words correctly.

Sentence Builder

Summary

A summary is a shortened version of the main points in your own words.

Activity ▶

Find page 10 in *Stacks of Stories*.

Read the paragraph beginning 'Mr Smike…'.

- Try reducing it to about one third of its length.
- Turn over this book and try it before you look at the example.

Help ▶

You can shorten by:

1 Summing up a number of things in one word. For example:

I like oranges, apples, bananas and grapes = **I like fruit**.

2 Cut out the unimportant bits such as examples and asides. For example:

It was, as I said to her at the time, a terrible mistake

= **It was a mistake**.

3 Cut out repeated bits. Just get the main point down. For example:

I don't like cheating. It's wrong. It's unfair. People shouldn't do it.

= **Cheating is wrong**.

Important – leave in.

Cross out – not important.

Cross out last *five* words – not necessary.

Cross out – not important.

Cross out – not important.

Mr Smike felt pleased with himself. He had told her, oh yes indeed.

You had to be firm with these cheeky young things. Briskly, he gathered up his papers, slipped them into his briefcase and clipped his pen into his breast pocket. He would finish the list at home. It would be something to look forward to after supper. Then, if there was time, he would write another of his complaining letters to the local paper. (Mr Smike wrote a lot of complaining letters to newspapers. It was a kind of hobby. He wrote about the state of the drains, the surliness of dustmen, the laziness of the unemployed and the trouble with Youth Today. If the paper didn't publish them, he wrote and complained about *that*.)

Shorten – He packed up his things.

Sum up: Later, he might write a letter of complaint to the newspaper – something he did often.

Writing Workshop

The plot thickens

Your aim today is to write an action-packed section of your story.

The bluish light is coming from a huge cavern. On the floor are two round disks. The light and the voices are coming from these. You see your two friends trapped inside, waving their arms and crying out, 'Get the crystal and set us free!' You turn and see the crystal on a rock in the middle of a dark, deep pool.

Help ▶▶

You may use these starters. They will help you to avoid repeating 'and then …and then…and then'.

First, I chose the…

Next, I…

When I had done that, I…

The important thing was…

I was afraid that…

There was a nasty moment when…

I had to…

At the last moment I…

Once I had done…

I told myself…

It was a moment I would…

Activity ▶

How can you get it? You see three things that might help – an empty oil drum, a long piece of rope and a large metal hook.

- Use these things to get over to the rock without falling in. Draw a picture to help you.

- Write down ten interesting verbs to describe your actions, such as: grabbed, leapt.

- Describe how you found the two disks then write an action-packed account of how you rescued the crystal.

Word Builder

Spelling check

In pairs, test each other on your own spellings from Unit Eight.

1 _____   6 _____

2 _____   7 _____

3 _____   8 _____

4 _____   9 _____

5 _____   10 _____

Unit Nine spellings

More family words.

What meanings link these words together besides their spelling?

A would   could   should

B also   almost   always

C before   between   below

   beneath   behind

D somehow   something   somewhere

   sometimes   somebody   someone

Investigating endings

Look at the word bank.

Use a pen to link up words with the same ending.

Activity ▷

musician	horrible	electrician	suitable	emotion
motion	lovable	education	incredible	lotion
possible	visible	magician	terrible	valuable
remarkable	election	politician	agreeable	creation

Activity ▷

- Now answer these questions:
1 Which endings sound like SHN?
2 Which of these endings is the most common way of writing an ending that sounds like SHN?
3 Which of these endings is used on words that end in IC?
4 What other ways are there of writing SHN? Give examples.
  (There aren't so many of these.)
5 There are three ways of telling whether a word should have an ABLE or an IBLE ending.
- Some people can hear the difference.
- Some people can do a trick with the word ABLE – can you work out what it is?
- You can look at what comes before the ending – can you work something that all the ABLE can do which the IBLE words cannot?
6 What other common endings can you think of? List examples and work out when the ending is likely to be used.

Vocabulary: Past tense

Most verbs end in ED when we put them into the past tense.

For example:

- **Drop → dropped**   - **Fill → filled**   - **Dance → danced**

Write down ten more examples.

Why do some words

- double the letter before ED?
- change the letter before ED?
- just add D?

Some verbs do it differently.

- In your workbook list the past tense for these verbs:

Present	do	eat	give	get	go	have	make	run	swim	say
Past										

- Can you think of more examples which do not use an ED ending?

Activity ▶▶

Change the following words into the past tense, then place them in the correct group at the bottom of the page.

wring   deal   spend   mean

send   burst   cut   hit

hurt   read   spread   catch

build   fight   seek   think

drive   rise   stride   sting

write   cling   swing   spin

No change	Change the middle vowel	Change end to UGHT	Add T	Change D to T

Detective Reader

The one who tells the tale

The narrator is the person telling the story.

- Sometimes the story is told as 'I' – it is written in the first person.
- Sometimes it is told by an outsider – it is written in the third person.
- Sometimes this outsider makes comments about the story, and sometimes he or she keeps quiet.

Activity ▷▷

- What can you work out about the narrators in these passages?

I was a bit shocked. I didn't say anything that bad. And I never thought a really tough girl like Justine would ever cry. I don't ever cry, no matter what.

The Story of Tracey Beaker **by Jacqueline Wilson**

February 15th

This is the worst day of my whole life. It began well. Joseph Hannibal left the house this morning at last. I thought he'd sail away on the evening tide and that would be the end of him. I was wrong. Billy has gone with him. Even as I write, I can hardly believe it. Billy has gone.

The Wreck of the Zanzibar **by Michael Morpurgo**

Help ▷▷

Sometimes the narrator is the main character in a story. In a **monologue**, the narrator is heard speaking. You can work out a lot about the narrator from the things they say and the way they say them.

He flew to the hole, clung to the edge, and poked his head up. A cool breeze played on his slick fur. He sang out and let the returning echo draw a picture in his head.

Silverwing **by Kenneth Oppel**

[It is winter]

Children – it's time to go home, so finish tidying up and put on your hats and coats. Some of our mummies are here for us, so hurry up.

Janey – I said help each other. Help Bobbie carry that chair, don't pin him against the wall with it.

Neville, off the floor, please. Don't lie there.

And Sidney, stop painting, please.

Because it's time to go home.

Well, you shouldn't have started another picture, should you.

What is it this time?

Another blue man! Oh, I see, so it is.

All right, you can make it just a little bit bluer, but only one more brushful, please, Sidney.

Neville, I said get up off the floor.

Who shot you dead?

David did? Well, I don't suppose he meant to. He may have meant to then, but he doesn't mean it now, and anyhow I say you can get up.

No, don't go and shoot David dead, because it's time to go home.

George. What did I tell you not to do? Well, don't do it.

And Sidney, don't wave that paint brush about like that, you'll splash somebody. LOOK OUT DOLORES!

From *George, Don't Do That* by Joyce Grenfell

Let's see, where were we? Oh, we'd got to where he had confessed his liking for fish. I wonder what else he likes. Does he like cucumbers? Yes, he does; he likes cucumbers. And potatoes? Yes, he likes potatoes too. Why, he's a regular old Nature-lover, that's what he is. I would have to come out to

dinner, and sit next to him. Wait, he's saying something! Words are simply pouring out of him. He's asking me if I'm fond of potatoes. No, I don't like potatoes. There, I've done it! I've differed from him. It's our first quarrel. He's fallen into a moody silence. Silly boy.

From *But the One on the Right* by Dorothy Parker

Activity ▶▶

- Where is the next narrator?
- What are we hearing?
- Is it a man or a woman and what is he or she like?

Agent X-Libris

We are investigating the use of animals as spies.

- Read this passage from *Fire, Bed and Bone* by Henrietta Branford.
- Prove that the narrator is a dog by finding five strong pieces of evidence in the passage.

I dreamed of how the house felt before the troubles came, when Alice was a baby, when Rufus was old already, but content, and Comfort loved him, and they slept together on a pallet stuffed with heather and I at their feet, and Alice beside us. I'd wake at night and pad across the earth floor to her cradle and look down at her to be sure that she was safe. Sometimes Rufus would wake and see me there and smile.

He would cuff the boys, but gently, if they pulled my tail or hurt my ears, and tell them they must treat me well, or else I'd never teach them how to hunt. He would set Alice on my back and Comfort would shake her head at him, and he would boast I was the gentlest dog in Christendom.

And he the gentlest master. I woke alone and sorrowful, and scraped out from under the rock and sat up on top of it with the cold stone sharp upon my pads. The world felt large and empty. Neither the sky above, nor the river, loud in the valley below, nor the wide, high dark offered any trace of Rufus. He was gone. I put my head back and shut my eyes and howled my want up to the black night.

I had seen him, standing on air among the shadow people. I had seen him tread the air again in Maidstone market place, upon the scaffold. I knew that I would not see him again.

I got down from the rock and said goodbye to Fleabane's puppy scent inside the den and turned my back on the valley and the village, on fire, bed and bone, on love and comfort and belonging. I took myself off into the wood, where the wild things and the outcasts dwell, where the trees gleam and rustle for mile upon green mile with a sound like water, and leaves hide wolf and bear and boar.

Fire, Bed and Bone by Henrietta Branford

Activity ▶▶

There are more than five characters in this story. Who are they?
- Draw matchstick figures and write under each one:
  - their name
  - their gender (male or female)
  - their age (roughly)
  - anything important you have found out about them.

Language Workout

Reading between the lines

Good readers behave like detectives. They put together hints and clues to build up a picture of what is happening.

> **Good readers:**
> - see pictures in their mind
> - hear a voice reading and characters speaking in their mind
> - guess what will happen next, and wait to see if it happens
> - reread bits when they get lost, or to check facts
> - ask questions and pass comments in their mind
> - spark off their own memories.

Read this passage from *I am the Cheese* by Robert Cormier:

I pedal furiously now, not because I want to catch up with them but because this road is deserted and I want to reach a better road or highway as soon as possible. I feel more vulnerable than ever. There are no houses in sight. Most of the cars use the Interstate that runs parallel to this old road. I keep pedalling. There's a curve ahead. Maybe there'll be a house or a new road or something around the curve.

I hear the car again. That unmistakable motor. The car is coming back. The car is rounding the curve, heading in my direction. The car's grille looks like the grinning mouth of some metal monster. The car is pink, a sickly pink, the kind of pink found in vomit. The car thunders by and I see the face of Whipper at the wheel and his grin is as evil and ferocious as the car's grille. The other two guys poke their heads out the window and laugh raucously as they go by.

I reach out and touch my father's package in the basket and I keep pedalling. There is nothing else to do but keep pedalling.

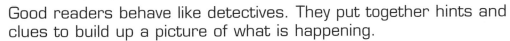

Activity ▶

- Look at the list of things a good reader does. Did you use any of them?
1 Write down five clues that tell you what country this story is set in.
2 Guess the age and sex of the narrator. Find three clues that suggest this.
3 Write down five clues that suggest the narrator is feeling very frightened.
4 Do you have an image of the setting in your mind? Draw a sketch map of the road based on information in the passage.
5 What do you think will happen next in the story? Find three clues in the passage to back you up.

- Now read the opening of *The Haunting* by Margaret Mahy.

When, suddenly, on an ordinary Wednesday, it seemed to Barney that the world tilted and ran down-hill in all directions, he knew he was about to be haunted again. It had happened when he was younger but he had thought that being haunted was a babyish thing that you grew out of, like crying when you fell over, or not having a bike.

'Remember Barney's imaginary friends, Mantis, Bigbuzz and Ghost?' Claire – his stepmother – sometimes said. 'The garden seems empty now that they've gone. I quite miss them.'

But she was really pleased perhaps because, being so very real to Barney, they had become too real for her to laugh over. Barney had been sorry to lose them, but he wanted Claire to feel comfortable living with him. He could not remember his own mother and Claire had come as a wonderful surprise, giving him a hug when he came home from school, asking him about his day, telling him about hers, arranging picnics and unexpected parties and helping him with hard homework. It seemed worth losing Mantis, Bigbuzz and Ghost and the other kind phantoms that had been his friends for so many days before Claire came.

Yet here it was beginning again … the faint dizzy twist in the world around him, the thin singing drone as if some tiny insect were trapped in the curling mazes of his ear. Barney looked up at the sky searching for a ghost but

there was only a great blueness like a weight pressing down on him. He looked away quickly, half expecting to be crushed into a sort of rolled-out gingerbread boy in an enormous stretched-out school uniform. Then he saw his ghost on the footpath beside him.

A figure was slowly forming out of the air: a child – quite a little one, only about four or five – struggling to be real. A curious pale face grew clearer against a halo of shining hair, silver gold hair that curled and crinkled, fading into the air like bright smoke. The child was smiling. It seemed to be having some difficulty in seeing Barney so that he felt that he might be the one who was not quite real. Well, he was used to feeling that. In the days before Claire he had often felt that he himself couldn't be properly heard or seen. But then Mantis had taken time to become solid and Ghost had always been dim and smoky. So Barney was not too surprised to see the ghost looking like a flat paper doll stuck against the air by some magician's glue. Then it became round and real, looking alive, but old-fashioned and strange, in its blue velvet suit and lace collar. A soft husky voice came out of it.

'Barnaby's dead!' it said. 'Barnaby's dead! I'm going to be very lonely.'

Activity ▶

- Go through the list again and discuss what you did in your mind when you were reading.
- Who is the narrator? What is happening? Find clues in the passage to back up your ideas.
- Choose one of the two passages and continue it in the same style. Give your readers hints and clues to get their imaginations going.

Challenge

Mix and match titles

Match the clues below to the titles in *Stacks of Stories*.

Clue	Actual Title
Eternal Existence	
Photographic Memory	
Dangerous Decapitation	
High-kicking Fun for the Younger Generation	
An Unusual Job, requiring a 'High-Flier'	
A Read from the Past	
Famous Composer's Favourite Fruit	
Shows Great Affection	
A Slippery Slope to the Past... or Future!	
A Challenge During an Unpleasant Vacation	
Tiny Planet	

Make up clues for:

Clue	Actual Title
	Charlie and the Chocolate Factory
	Snow White and the Seven Dwarfs
	The Magic Faraway Tree
	The Hare and the Tortoise

Now make up clues for four more books then swap clues to see if another group can guess them.

Sentence Builder

Speech marks

In 'A Career In Witchcraft', in the *Stacks of Stories* book,
the characters spend much of the story speaking to each other.

Activity ▶▶

- If you haven't read the story before, read up to the end of page 7.
- If you have read it before, begin at 'There isn't one' (on page 4) and read to the end of page 7.

1 On pages 6 and 7, there are pictures of two characters. Next to each picture, write the last thing the character said in a speech bubble.

2 When you write a sentence, the job of the speech bubble is done by speech marks. Speech marks pick out the actual words spoken.

Written below is part of the discussion between the two characters. Discuss what could go in the spaces to make it clearer who is speaking.

'Got anythin' new on toads?' persisted _____

'No!' _____

'Bats?' _____

'No!' _____

'Anythin' that'll tell me where to get an eye of newt?'

_____

- Read pages 8 and 9, and then complete the following rules:

  1 Speech marks show _____ .

  2 All punctuation in speech goes on the _____ hand side of the speech mark.

  3 We use paragraphs in speech to show when _____ .

  4 You don't need a comma if there is _____ .

Writing Workshop

A satisfying ending

Your aim today is to complete your story with a satisfying ending.

Activity ▷▷

Plan, and then write the ending. Include the following:

1 How you use the crystal to free your friends.
2 What you say and what they tell you.
3 How you run from the cave.
4 Getting your bikes and how you all felt at that moment.
5 Your final thoughts as you look back on the adventure.

Help ▷▷

- When you have the crystal, imagine the reunion with your friends.
- Describe your feelings as you see them again.
- Make them tell you what happened to them.
- End your story as you emerge from the cave into the wood, daylight and freedom!

Word Builder

Spelling check

Test yourself on the spellings from Unit Nine. The teacher will read them out.

A _____

_____

_____

B _____

_____

_____

C _____

_____

_____

D _____

_____

_____

_____

The NO words

Look at the word bank. There are four prefixes you can use to say NO, UNDO, or DO THE OPPOSITE.

Word Bank

DIS	DE	UN	ANTI
disinfect	defrost	unamused	anticlockwise
dismount	defuse	unnecessary	antiseptic
disagree	degenerate	unpaid	anticlimax
dissatisfied	decompose	untidy	antibiotic

Activity ▷

- Which prefix means REVERSE THE PROCESS?
- Which prefix means SOMETHING HASN'T HAPPENED YET?
- Why does DISSATISFIED have two Ss and UNNECESSARY have two Ns?

- Which other prefix gives the opposite of many words starting with M and P?

    _____ moral

    _____ mortal

    _____ mobile

    _____ proper

    _____ possible

    _____ plausible

- Which other prefix gives the opposite of many words starting with R?

    _____ reversible

    _____ reverent

    _____ regular

Vocabulary: Family and gender

Make a list of things which have different words for male and female. Examples:

Male	Female
man	woman
fox	vixen
he	she

Complete the vocabulary table and add three examples of your own:

Animal	Home	Male	Female	Young	Collective	Sound
cow	stall	bull	cow	calf	herd	moo
horse						
			nanny-goat			
				puppy		
						purr
	eyrie					
			vixen			
bear						
	sty					
						bleat

Detective Reader

The moral of the story

The **moral** of the story is its message. Most stories end so that good characters are rewarded and bad characters are punished. People who are evil, greedy and violent get their come uppance. Stories are often about the way the characters become better people.

Aesop was a Greek writer who lived 2000 years ago. He wrote fables which are stories with a strong message or moral. The reader is meant to learn something from them.

A dog was carrying a large piece of meat in his mouth and feeling very pleased with himself. He walked across the fields and through the woods until he came to a bridge across a stream. As he was walking across he looked down and saw another dog, just like him with a piece of meat, just like his. It was his own reflection but the dog did not realise this. As the dog looked, he felt more and more unhappy.

'That dog has a piece of meat like mine only his is much bigger,' he said. The dog became very jealous. He decided that his own piece of meat was not good enough and he would drop it so that he could take the other dog's piece of meat.

Splash! He dropped his own piece of meat into the water and then he saw what a fool he had been. There was no other dog and there was no other meat. His meat was now at the bottom of the stream. The dog went home with nothing.

Adapted from *Aesop's Fables*

Activity ▷

- Which of these is the moral of the story?
  Laugh and the world laughs with you.
  Don't eat your lunch near a river.
  Eat your food up right away.
  Be content with what you have.
  Love makes the world go round.
- Why did you reject the other four?

What is the moral of this story?

A mouse accidentally ran across a sleeping lion's face and woke him up. The lion was very angry but the mouse begged for mercy.

'Please don't kill me. I may be able to help you one day,' said the mouse.

The good-natured lion laughed at the idea that a mouse could ever help him and let the mouse go.

That night the lion was captured by hunters. They tied him with rope and left him while they went to eat. The mouse saw the lion and nibbled through the ropes with his sharp teeth until the lion was free.

Adapted from *Aesop's Fables*

Discuss what point the story is trying to make and write down the moral.

Agent X-Libris

Your last mission! We want to find stories with something important to say about how we live our lives. Read 'Karate for Kids' by Terence Blacker in *Stacks of Stories* and write down what you think the moral of the story is. You can have more than one answer.

Language Workout

Endings

Proverbs

Proverbs are wise sayings. Link up the proverbs on the left with the meanings on the right. The first one is done for you.

Proverbs

- Least said, soonest mended.
- Many hands make light work.
- Out of the frying pan, into the fire.
- A stitch in time saves nine.
- Don't count your chickens before they are hatched.
- He who laughs last, laughs longest.
- Too many cooks spoil the broth.
- Don't put all your eggs in one basket.
- One good turn deserves another.
- Look before you leap.

Meaning

- One good person can get the job done quicker.
- A job is easier if more people help.
- Check before you rush into things.
- Don't jump to conclusions.
- Help those who help you.
- Be careful not to move to something even worse.
- The best way to patch up a quarrel is not to talk about it.
- Don't pin all your hopes on just one thing.
- Don't be put off by critics, but make sure you win in the end.
- Don't put it off, put it right.

Activity ▶

- Discuss the meaning of the following proverbs:

  Honesty is the best policy.

  Actions speak louder than words.

  Look before you leap.

  Laughter is the best medicine.

  More haste, less speed.

- Write a short fable, like Aesop's, with a proverb as a moral. Read aloud your stories to each other and try to guess the moral.

- Discuss the meaning of the proverb 'You can't judge a book by its cover.' How might this apply to people?

A story

The new boy at school looked a shocker. He was dropped off a motorbike driven by his long-haired brother. His brother roared straight across the pedestrian crossing and nearly knocked over Mrs Morris, who was on duty.

The new boy didn't just walk in the front gate, like anyone else. He swaggered in as if he owned the place, and booted Johnny Marshall's football so hard against the school wall, you could see it shudder. The ball rebounded and hit Mrs Morris just as she was coming in, recovering from the motorbike incident outside. The new boy didn't even notice. He sat down and pulled out a newspaper from his battered school bag.

Mrs Morris, who was our form tutor, told us she had an important announcement. 'A new boy will be joining us today,' she said brightly. 'His name is Jason and he's been to a few schools before ours.'

She took a deep breath and glanced at the door, where Jason's huge frame could be seen through the glass. 'But that doesn't mean he's a bad boy and I want everyone to make Jason feel at home.'

The door burst open. Jason advanced to the centre of the room.

Activity ▷

- Now think how you can develop the story to illustrate the proverb 'You can't judge a book by its cover.'
    - How does Jason behave when he comes in?
    - Who does he sit next to?
    - How does he react to the class?
    - What happens during the day to show 'You can't judge a book by its cover'? Try to think up one main incident that shows Jason in a different light.
- Write the rest of the story.
- Now think about a different moral:
'Leopards can't change their spots.'
Discuss the meaning of this old saying.
- How could you change the story you have just written to illustrate this saying? How would the ending change?
- Look at the other proverbs and see if any of them could be used as the moral to the story. Tell the changed story to the class and see if they can guess the right moral.

Challenge

Mix and match titles

Study the titles of the first three books, then make up some of your own:

Carpet Craft

by
Walter Wall Carpetin

Death on the Cliff

by Eileen Dover

Improving your Garden

by Moses Lawn

Now try rearranging the letters in a name to spell ne words.
For example:

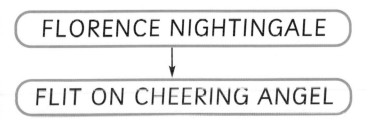

FLORENCE NIGHTINGALE

↓

FLIT ON CHEERING ANGEL

Activity ▶

Can you do this with your name, or the name of someone else in the class?

Sentence Builder

Bend me, shape me

Sentences are like plasticene. You can make them, break them, shape them, change them. You can cut them down, stretch them out, and make them what you want them to be. That is what writing is all about.

Here is the opening of *Fantastic Mr Fox* by Roald Dahl.

THE THREE FARMERS

Down in the valley there were three farms. The owners of these farms had done well. They were rich men. They were also nasty men. All three of them were about as nasty and mean as any men you could meet. Their names were Farmer Boggis, Farmer Bunce and Farmer Bean.

Boggis was a chicken farmer. He kept thousands of chickens. He was enormously fat. This was because he ate three boiled chickens smothered with dumplings every day for breakfast, lunch and supper.

Activity >>

1 There are ten sentences. Join them together and make them into three.

2 Cut the new sentences down to about half their length.

3 Change the order of each sentence around. At least three words must move in each sentence. You can add in one or two words if this helps.

4 Change the order of the sentences themselves and link them together in a new way.

5 Swap eight words for new words.(It may change the meaning completely – that's okay.)

6 Compare your new passage with those of other people.

- Try this again with the two paragraphs on page 130 of *Stacks of Stories* beginning 'She turned on the engine' up to 'cheering the library on.'

- Try it with some sentences from your own story, and see how much difference you can make.

Writing Workshop

A book jacket

Today's aim is to design a cover for your story. Look at books in your classroom.

Activity ▷▷

- Think of eight things that appear on most book jackets. Write them in the boxes next to the cover, below.

- Discuss what makes you want to read a book from its cover, and make a list here:

  _____   _____

  _____   _____

  _____   _____

- Now think about the cover for your own story.
  - What will you put in it to make a reader want to read it?
  - How will you attach the pages to the cover?
  - Make a rough sketch first, then make the cover and put your booklet together.

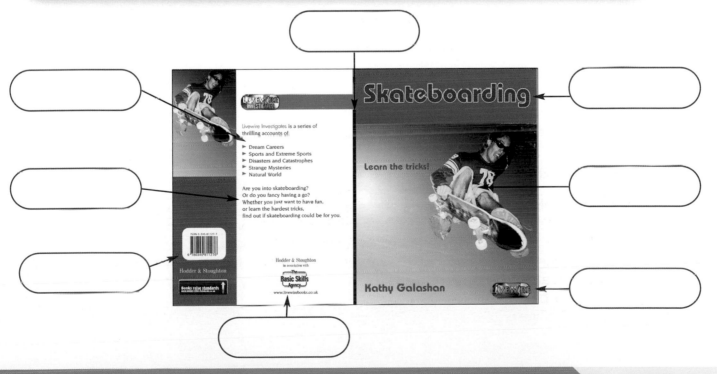

ANSWERS

Unit One: Thief! (page 9)

The thief was Donald 'Deadleg' Malone.

He had no alibi for the time of the theft; he fits the description. He does have a limp. The 'Don' on his key fob could have been misread as 'Alan' if seen briefly. A crook that sold the trophies on paid him £500. He lives only 10 minutes from the school and could have easily committed the crime.

Unit Three: Quick-fire quiz (page 38)

Air hostess	Knife
Biscuit	Lift
Curry	Milk
Diver	Number
Expert	Oar
Fire	Petal
Genius	Queue
Hair	Reward
Insect	Shampoo
Jam	

Unit Eight: Story continuation (page 91)

This is how the mystery continues:

Somehow Dolly knew it must be the same man who had made the footprints. He must have known that they were following him all the time and deliberately led them to this field. She had to think quickly. They might be able to run but they would never get over the barbed wire fence before he caught up with them. Their only chance was to run into the barn.